Relational Music Therapy:
An Intersubjective Perspective

Gro
Trondalen

Barcelona PUBLISHERS

Relational Music Therapy:
An Intersubjective Perspective

Print ISBN: 9781937440183
E-ISBN: 9781937440190

Barcelona Publishers
10231 Plano Road
Dallas TX 75238
www.barcelonapublishers.com
SAN 298-6299

Written with support from
The Norwegian Non-fiction Writers and Translators Association.

Cover Photo: © 2016 Annette Øvrelid
Cover design: © 2016 Frank McShane

Copy-Editor: Jack Burnett

To Hanna and Hallvard

Acknowledgments

I recall an early breakfast on a dark November morning in 1994 at Old Vraa Castle in Denmark. Ken Bruscia encouraged me to do a Ph.D., even though I was only in the initial phase of my master's degree in music therapy. Two decades later, Barcelona Publishers, with Ken at the forefront, is publishing the present book. I am deeply grateful.

Unni Tanum Johns has been a close colleague and friend for many years, and an intersubjective and dialoguing "sister." Her wisdom, laughter, and attentiveness in the here-and-now encourages me in my life. Even Ruud, supervisor, colleague, and friend, offered me space to develop my personal way into music therapy; a "fellow traveller" emerged. Shaping thoughts and visions with the esteemed colleagues and friends at the Centre for Research in Music and Health (CREMAH), Karette Stensæth (Norway) and Lars Ole Bonde (Denmark), has truly influenced me as a researcher and leader. Denise Grocke (Australia) and Cheryl Dileo (USA) have inspired, supported, and encouraged me, not least to publish more in English. Diane Maris (South Africa) entered my life when I least expected it, as did Anne Margrethe Hjelvik (Norway). Also, thanks to colleagues and students at the music therapy trainings in Oslo and Sandane/Bergen for the inspiring questions and reflections they have offered over the last 25 years.

The book includes a list of references. I am grateful to the authors for providing their texts in public. In addition, I am aware of my indebtedness to the lectures, conference papers, and small talks I have had with family, friends, peers, students, and clients. These dialogues constantly make me re-think and re-search music therapy. I have done my very best to give credit to my "stepping stones", the people who have provided me with living memories and stimulating perspectives on music therapy. Thank you.

I could not have managed without my closest family and their support and encouragement. Hanna and Hallvard, my grown children, are teaching me the most important things in life by being themselves. My husband Dag's love and belief in me are fundamental to my life. My grandchildren, Aurora and Ask, are continuously showing me the power of immediacy and a genuine presence, while reminding me of how blessed I am to be part of a life circle. That circle also includes my parents, Marit and Bjarne, who always have supported me.

Thanks to the Norwegian Non-fiction Writers and Translators Association for granting me a scholarship to work on this book, and to my employer, the Norwegian Academy of Music, for support in writing it.

Last but not least, I wish to thank the clients who have given me their informed consent to publish their music therapy stories. During the process of writing, a renewed gratefulness to each of them, from whom I have learned so much, has emerged.

Table Of Contents

Preface

This book is an encouragement to seize the *intersubjective, relational music experience* and explore the power of such a musical presence. The text addresses lived experiences, specifically, relational lived experiences in a joint musicianship between client(s) and a music therapist, exemplified through professional music therapy practice.

Two decades ago, Daniel Stern gave a lecture that has greatly influenced my theoretical understanding and development as a music therapy practitioner and researcher. The lecture in question was given to a meeting of the Nordic Network for Music Therapy Research (Pedersen & Mahns, 1996), on the topic "How Do People Change in Psychotherapy through Non-Verbal Means?" Stern (1996) focused on "hot present moments," which he later termed "moments of meeting" (Stern, 1998). He suggested that major changes is the result of a series of microscopic changes that result from therapeutic involvement processes within a given time span, be it a moment or a microsecond. To me, the lecture served as an eye-opener and confirmation of the importance of microprocesses in therapy and in life generally. Stern's presentation, rooted in lived experience, presented a close interweaving of theoretical and clinical phenomena that genuinely resonated with me. As a music therapist working within a non-verbal modality, I could relate to Stern's model of a layered development of sense of self (Stern, 2000). It offered me, as a music therapist, useful ways of thinking both at a theoretical and a practical level (Trondalen, 2013d).

Whereas Stern's (2000) model of development emerged from psychoanalysis and developmental psychology, the present book is on music therapy. Relational music therapy highlights an intersubjective perspective, indicating how therapeutic change may come about through non-verbal processes at the micro level in music therapy. The text illustrates its observations through examples of psychotherapeutic work in individual and group settings in mental health care, including expressive and receptive music therapy methods. Interpretative phenomenology provides the scientific basis, while exploring philosophical, theoretical, and clinical sources, for engaging with the nature of music therapy microprocesses. I hope that this book will be of interest to theoreticians and clinicians alike.

I have translated the clients' comments into English. All the clients were speakers of Scandinavian languages; with some of them who were not Scandinavian natives, English has served as a supporting language in music therapy. To protect the clients' anonymity, I have not revealed their citizenships, nor have I used their real names.

It has been a most wonderful—and challenging—journey to write and reflect upon the present text. During this process, I have often wondered if it is possible to understand *relation as an overarching form* in music therapy with reference to non-verbal, practical, theoretical, and philosophical levels. It might be so. The issue at stake is to seize the relational music moment. It includes non-verbal (implicit) knowledge at a micro level as an agent of change and reorientation, i.e., development and change through an expansion of the musical intersubjective field to optimize the client's health.

Gro Trondalen
Oslo, Norway
8 March 2016

Relational Music Therapy:
An Intersubjective Perspective

Introduction

Music therapy is a relatively recent discipline, profession, and practice. This is true even though the oldest account of medical practices, the Kahum papyrus (1825 BCE), describes the use of chants for healing, and even though references to therapeutic uses of music appear throughout Eastern and Western history to the present day. Skepticism in medical-historical texts concerning the actual importance of music (Horgen, 2000) has limited the impact of this tradition on the development of music therapy today. Therapists and scholars alike can appreciate music's connection to various views of illness and recovery and of the healing forces at play. Such attitudes, however, reveal much more about their original cultural contexts than they do about any universal capacity of music. The belief systems and musical healing rituals of other times and places represent a great legacy, but they cannot be transferred directly to contemporary contexts (Bonde, 2014; Gouck, 2000).

Music therapy as a formal discipline developed after World War II and acquired its modern form in the United States, with the first training course in that country being offered in 1944. The development of music therapy continued in both the United States and Europe and accelerated during the late 1950s in Austria and the United Kingdom. The early 1960s and 1970s were pioneering years for music therapy in many countries, and the 1980s and 1990s saw the further professionalism of related services and the formalization of related education and research (Bunt & Stige, 2014). Maranto (1993) identified 14 educational models in the United States alone, encompassing more than a hundred different therapy techniques. At the Ninth World Congress of Music Therapy in Washington in 1999, the scientific committee provided a special track highlighting five international models of music therapy practice (Wheeler, 2012). Those models of music therapy are still developing (Bruscia, 2014a).

Aigen (2014, p. 220) suggested a number of orientations (from 1982), identified as a Stage Three Music Therapy Orientations. The present volume explores a possible contribution to this grouping of orientations. An intersubjective perspective on relational music therapy views communication as an ongoing process with different levels. It assumes that everybody has an inherent human ability to share thoughts, experiences, and actions through music, enabling us to become engaged in the lives of others at an existential level (Trondalen, 2008).

The music therapy landscape is not fixed but constantly in motion (Bonde, 2015; Ruud, 2016). As a discipline, a profession, and a professional practice (Stige, 2003), whatever its theoretical or clinical orientation, music therapy does have some common values. It can be a complementary or an integrative practice, or it can be a primary means of treatment, as illustrated by Bruscia's (1998) categorizations. It is also multilayered, as both a science and an art form (Wigram, Saperston, & West, 1995). As an art form, music therapy involves subjectivity, individuality, creativity, and beauty. As a science, it involves objectivity, documentation, reliability, validity, and truth. Lastly, as an interpersonal process, it involves empathy, intimacy, communication, mutuality, and relationship.

Interpretative Phenomenology

The present volume focuses on modern developmentally informed theory, highlighting intersubjectivity within a contextual framework. The philosophical basis for exploring lived musical experiences is hermeneutics (Alvesson & Sköldberg, 1994) and phenomenology (Van Manen, 1990). These two philosophical perspectives seemingly rooted in different paradigms, both concern meaning. However, reality is manifold, as is the term *meaning*. Ontologically, it can be argued that the two philosophies of science cannot be merged. This book, however, seeks to explore approaches that consider the fundamental relational perspective. It is not a philosophical investigation per se. On this basis, the following elaboration discusses some key words found in the two philosophies of science. I suggest that an *interpretative phenomenology* (Smith, Flowers, & Larkin, 2009) is a useful basis for an intersubjective perspective on relational music therapy, as the practice of relating experiences through music unfolds.

Phenomenology is searching for the essential structures or essence of lived experience by bracketing the person's beliefs about the phenomenon (i.e., epoché). There is a focus on individual and contextual independence when perceiving, for example, musical processes or when performing musical analysis. The phenomenon itself emerges. Phenomenology appears to be without any theoretical foundation or consideration (Husserl, 1999). Hermeneutics may be understood as a counterpoint to phenomenology, with its focus on the understanding and interpretation of musical processes based on personal, historical, cultural, and literary contexts. Reality is constructed and interpreted on basis of our pre-understanding, in a circular alternation between parts and wholes, of the phenomenon being studied and interpreted. A researcher or clinician may describe a musical improvisation rooted in the client's perception but may also add her own understanding of the musical processes. Accordingly, she constructs reality based on knowledge, language, and historical situatedness (Alvesson & Sköldberg, 1994). Both phenomenology and hermeneutics are process-oriented approaches. They are elaborations of meaning, supporting a belief in a subjective consciousness, in addition to an affirmation of—and attention toward—the perception of the physical world.

An important basis for a relational form of music therapy is the living body. The phenomenology of the body states that the body is our primary source of knowledge and the subject of all our actions (Merleau-Ponty, 1962). The mind emerges and exists from intrinsic self-organizing processes and interacts with other minds. "One of the consequences of this view of 'embodied cognition' is that the mind is, by nature, 'intersubjectively open,' as it is partially constituted through interactions with other minds." (Stern, 2004, p. 95).

In expressive music therapy, the client and the music therapist use their bodies to sing or perform on instruments while expressing themselves at the same time. That means that they are maintaining a subjective relation to themselves and to their instrument while also reaching out to another. The process is similar in receptive music therapy, such as in the Bonny Method of Guided Imagery and Music (GIM). The client is both perceiving and grasping the interactive musical relationship during a listening procedure. The work of reflection and action represents a form of mutuality, but the two never merge completely. Such a phenomenological point of reference treats the self as a basic category of being in the world, linking the client and the music therapist to their experiences and their contexts (Nerheim, 1995). These various positions in the world imply that the client and the music therapist relate to each other through different positions. At a practical level, the two of them have a joint though not identical experience in the musical relationship. The *lived experience* is at the forefront, as it emerges through the music therapy relationship. This phenomenal relationship is interactive in nature and interpreted within the therapeutic context.

***

Having offered this brief overview of the changing landscape of music therapy and interpretative phenomenology, I will next turn to the notions of the relational turn and intersubjectivity, which form the basis for shifting from a one-person to a two-person model of human development. I then discuss development as a dialogical continuum, followed by an explanation of core terms within an intersubjective perspective on relational music therapy, such as implicit relational knowing, synchronization, affect attunement, in addition to affect integration and mentalization. Furthermore, the text elaborates on our understanding of self, intersubjectivity, and recognition before turning to the music therapy relationship and the relational music therapist. Included within the latter topic is a section on self-care for the relational music therapist. Related philosophical life-world existentials are investigated, including the phenomena of playing, followed by musical intersubjecitity. Finally, the text concentrates on power, responsibility, and ethics. The volume illustrates both expressive and receptive music therapy methods in mental health care.

Chapter 1

The Relational Turn

The notion of the "relational turn" forms the basis for shifting from a one-person ("monadic") to a two-person ("dialogic") model of human development. A relational perspective provides concepts *within a paradigm* rather than one single, unified theory. Current relational perspectives derive from self-psychology, developmental psychology, attachment theory, neuro-psychoanalysis, interpersonal, object relations theory, social constructivism, feminism, and new Marxism (Binder, Nielsen, Vøllestad, Holgersen, & Schanche, 2006). Focusing on changes in therapy by way of developmentally informed theories is not a new endeavor, particularly with regard to psychodynamic traditions (Hansen, 1996). However, during the 1970s and 1980s the *empirical* evidence for development made a quantum leap, thanks to research on infants' ability to engage in reciprocity and contact (Bateson, 1975). Technical inventions enabled detailed observations and analyses at a micro level (Stern, 1971; Trevarthen, 1980). In-depth studies provided crucial understanding of the phenomena of interactions (Hansen, 1991b). Video analyses of microprocesses (i.e., microscopic changes from moment to moment) revealed a heretofore unrecognized *competent* child, someone who could adjust to and influence her or his surroundings and initiate actions or respond actively in early interactive processes (Beebe, Knoblauch, Rustin, & Sorter, 2005). The infant was clearly an active co-creator of its personal and the other's intrapersonal and interpersonal worlds (Bråten, 1998; Tronick, 1989).

According to Havnesköld and Mothander (1995/1997), psychological theory develops in trends or waves that they label, for example, as theory of drives, ego-psychological theory, object relations theory, self-psychology, and affective theory. The present volume cannot provide a comprehensive overview of such historical developments; rather, I am primarily interested in what happened when studies of infant and early interaction prompted a comprehensive reassessment of the individual's sensory capacity and mutual participation in social exchange. At the very core of this leap forward is the person's capacity for social interaction, which was demonstrated through detailed descriptions of microprocesses in daily life and in therapeutic settings (Boston Change Process Study Group, 2010). Biological phenomena and the psychological experience revealed themselves as two sides of the same coin, and the perceived split between soma and psyche appeared false (Bernth, 1995/1997). Hence, development is understood as a procedural, dialogical construction process with *feelings* described as the primary agent. Meaning and coherence are therefore constituted through an active co-creation and interplay with other fellow beings by way of intersubjective sharing and interaction (Stern, 1995).

In terms of understanding, there has been a shift from perceiving the individual as a clinical construction ("the clinical infant") toward seeing the person as she or he appears through empirical observations ("the observed infant") (Stern, 1985, p. 14). The former "clinical infant" understands adult psychopathology based on a retrospective perspective. That is, the psychoanalytic "clinical infant" arises via the client's own recollections, recreated through transference work in a therapeutic setting and interpreted in a theoretical framework. The "observed infant," on the other hand, is the physical individual as she or he appears directly.

These complementary notions act to clarify the difference between a clinical understanding of the individual, based on reconstruction through psychoanalytic theory, and the person who emerges from video observations or from experimental and longitudinal studies (Havnesköld & Mothander, 1995/1997). None of the terms, however, indicates how it *feels* to experience social interaction or elaborates in depth as to how inner motives or subjective content are structurally organized.

The terms *clinical infant* and *observed infant* are reconciled through the hypothesis of the individual's subjective experience. This model, based on observation, is more normative than disease-based and tends to look forward more than backward. It acknowledges the

8

fact that certain aspects of perceptions of self may predict later pathology, but this is not the goal of this model, according to Stern (1985, p. 20):

> In contrast, the approach taken here is normative rather than pathomorphic and prospective rather than retrospective. While disruptions in the development of any sense of self may prove to be predictive of later pathology, the different senses of self are designed to describe normal development and not to explain the ontogeny of pathogenic forms.

I cultivate a normative and prospective perspective in this text as well. Consequently, some of the background for observing musical processes at a general level seems important. I do not limit myself to looking for pathological aspects within the music or the musical performance. Instead, my perspective actively focuses on supporting creative health resources in the here and now.

In the present context, a relational turn includes an intersubjective perspective that encompasses human development as a continuum, while drawing attention to both non-verbal (implicit) and verbal (explicit) modes of knowledge. There is a particular focus on the emergence and co-creation of interpersonal meaning through music as a non-verbal means of communication. This embraces a focus on affective communication. In addition, experiences in expressive and receptive music therapy may be verbally explored and narrated on the basis of a joint experience that supports development from regulation to reflecting function.

Drawing on infant research as a basic premise for understanding music therapy processes is not the same as saying that infants and adults are identical. Still, I am swayed by the possibility that modern developmentally informed theories based on infant research can inform perception of non-verbal and unconscious microprocesses in music therapy for everyone. Hence, a dialogical and relational perspective in the clinical setting counts for an affective awareness, which is of crucial importance. This means an emphasis on experience rather than explicit knowledge in therapy, that is, on seeing therapy as a means of enriching and deepening one's experience rather than as an end in itself. These non-verbal and unconscious experiences through music form the basis of a potential verbal investigation in music therapy, which supports creation of a personal narrative (mentalization). The verbal conversation can expand the meaning of the interplay between the therapist and the client, but does not substitute for the phenomenological lived experience of meaning at a non-verbal level.

Chapter 2

Intersubjectivity

The understanding of relational music therapy proposed in this book follows the path of intersubjectivity. The concept of intersubjectivity has been around for the better part of a century (Thompson, 2005). Philosophically, it has its roots in the existential and phenomenological thinking of Husserl and Merleau-Ponty, focusing on human community and the lived experience to be able to experience meaning. From a phenomenological perspective, intersubjectivity labels the human's subjective being in the world as intentional (Husserl, 1999). That is, consciousness is always directed towards something. The mind is by nature intersubjectively dependent and open. Human beings are dialogical and intentional from the beginning. The human body is a carrier of subjectivity that recognizes the other as a body subject, the significance of bodily phenomena being in the forefront. Being in time together in the here-and-now mode is necessary to establish an intersubjective relationship .

At a theoretical level, the term intersubjectivity is used within different domains of knowledge in the interest of exploring the human being (Blom & Wrangsjö, 2013; Stensæth & Trondalen, 2012). There are however, different foci when presenting the phenomenon of intersubjectivity. Historically, the theoretical perspective on intersubjective has been presented in three ways (Hansen, 1996).

First, the intersubjective relationship can be considered as a meeting between intrapsychic and interpersonal conditions, that is, as a framework for relational transference and countertransference (Mitchell & Aron, 1999; Stolorow, Atwood, & Brandtchaft, 1994/2004). Second, Benjamin (1990) challenged the psychoanalytic notion of object relationship, claiming that the recognition of subjectivity was a necessary condition for change. She characterized the psychoanalytic process as an oscillation between intrapsychic fantasies and intersubjective recognition. Finally, the third presentation of intersubjectivity resonates with modern developmentally informed psychology; according to this view, intersubjectivity is typified by an interpersonal, mutually created and shared world of meaning (Bråten, 1998; Stern, 1985; Trevarthen, 1980). The individual's immediate, intentional, and joint synchronization with the other's mind happens through direct exchanges of affects and joint attention, which create a dialogical frame of development (Bruner, 1975). The present intersubjective perspective on relational music therapy is linked to this third understanding.

Intersubjectivity concerns creating mental contact (Stern, 2004). Such mental contact is non-verbal (implicit) and happens within a procedural framework. Experience, body, and affects are core elements. Affective non-verbal expressions are vital and take priority when we are talking about experiences of what we feel and think. Intersubjectivity connects to the here-and-now, within a local context (Hansen, 2010). It is more about seeing and perceiving than about searching for explicit meaning (Stern, 2004). Intersubjective participation develops from concrete interplay (regulation) toward an ability to create meaning about oneself and others (mentalization).

Stern (2000) refers to Trevarthen and Hubley's (1978) operationalization of intersubjectivity as "a deliberately sought sharing of experiences about events and things." Intersubjectivity emerges from fundamental human self-organizing processes during interactions with others that allow recognition of each other's minds. Intersubjective openness emerges "from mechanisms such as mirror neurons, adaptive oscillators, and other similar processes" (Stern, 2004, p. 95). Infants are by nature prepared to encounter "virtual others" (Bråten, 1998) within the intersubjective matrix. Three mental states are evident in intersubjectivity: joint attention, sharing of intentions, and affective states (Stern, 2000). These mental states can be shared without translation into language, and they occur in both expressive and receptive music therapy.

At a practical level, intersubjectivity encompasses a mental state of awareness and exchange of affects in the here-and-now. Imitation and interpersonal synchronization processes at the micro level play a significant part in intersubjectivity. The flow of mental states (experiencing each other mentally) happens within moment-to-moment contact. This contact is *crossmodal* or *amodal*, meaning that the exploration of the interplay may occur across different modalities as the persons continue to relate to each other. It is a contact on the basis of form and contour within a time span (Hansen, 2010). The flow of experiencing each other very often occurs in different modalities. It includes implicit and procedural knowing, and has experience, body and affects at its center.

Intersubjectivity relates to a local context, to microprocesses in the here-and-now. The dyad negotiates meaning at different levels through "errors and repairs" (Tronick, 1989), on the basis of its subjective capacity. Hence, intersubjectivity is understood in three ways. The first two are as (1) a *domain* (of development) or (2) an *inborn capacity* and disposition (or "motif"; Trevarthen, 1980), that is, a *relational dimension in itself* ("an intersubjective matrix"; Stern, 2004). These moment-to-moment meetings are rooted in each of the participants' minds. The persons are, however, something more than two separate subjects or minds (Stern et.al., 1998). Each participant's ways of being with the other are exposed to influences. Such a flow of mutual exchange supports the creation of the third form of intersubjectivity, an *intersubjective field* (Tronick, 1998), which has as its very core experience, body, and affects in the here-and-now. An exploration of the intersubjective field supports change, which happens through meetings with others' minds.

A mutual interaction aims at creating joint meaning in such a way that similarities and differences can be explored and shared. At the center is the assumption that an *expansion* of self-experience, self-understanding, and joint meaning leads to subjective and intersubjective change. From this point of view, expansion of the intersubjective field means a development from concrete interplay to the creation of meaning between oneself and others. Intersubjective meaning can be experienced at different layers and in a variety of modes. One vital example of a meaningful co-creation within the frame of intersubjectivity is performed through musical elements, for example, movements, rhythms, and dynamic shifts (Bjørkvold, 1989; Johns, 1993).

Intersubjectivity involves an experience of "I know that you know that I know" and "I feel that you feel that I feel." It entails an appraisal or reading of the content of the other person's mind.

> Such readings can be mutual. Two people see and feel
> roughly the same mental landscape for a moment at least.
> These meetings are what psychotherapy is largely about.
> They also provide the happenings that change our lives
> and become the memories that compose the story of our
> intimate relationships. (Stern, 2004, p. 75)

In line with this knowledge, a main goal for music therapy is to expand the client's lived experience and intersubjective awareness through new ways of relating through music. The therapist's emotional availability and responsiveness, in addition to attention, regulation of emotions, and reflexivity, are of vital importance in such a musical approach. Active mutual co-creation and interplay with other human beings make meaning and encourage coherence. Intersubjective sharing and interplay are basic in such a dialogical matrix (Malloch & Trevarthen, 2009). The caregiver's emotional availability and positive feelings (Siegel, 1999) in addition to the importance of play, are incentives for participation and action (Emde, 1990).

Interpersonal togetherness through attunement is important for meaning-making activity. Through affect attunement, the person experiences what can be shared and what remains isolated. Accordingly, the participant experiences both the form and the degree of what can be shared in an intersubjective universe. Stern calls the attunement process the mainstay of intersubjectivity, whereas dynamic forms of vitality are grounding pillars (Stern, interviewed by Heje & Johansen, 1990). Vitality is a "manifestation of life, of being alive," Stern says (2010, p. 3). We experience people in terms of their vitality, and the vital relationship itself creates new possibilities for action. Moments of intersubjective creation are special present moments and constitute a potential healing force, allowing new feelings to emerge and be explored.

An intersubjective meeting involves sharing joint but not identical experiences. What is shared is, of course, linked to the relationship and context in a broad sense, whether the partners are a mother and child or an adult client and a therapist. It is not easy to discover or describe intersubjectivity in a relationship. Interestingly, "A curious property with intersubjectivity is that it seems to be easier to note when it's not present" (Børstad, 1992, p. 115). A breakdown in intersubjectivity, then (for example, through traumatic events), very often leads to isolation and loneliness. Obviously, intersubjectivity is basic to our existence.

An intersubjective field can emerge through any musical activity, be it receptive or expressive, through which participants allow for experiencing the world and themselves through a particular kind of relationship. This relationship is a musical moving-along process involving the regulation of emotion and affects at a non-verbal level, one in which microprocesses play a crucial role. This relationship is expressed in a communicative structure that gives pre-verbal language dialogic meaning (Hansen, 1991a). A verbal conversation in music therapy can increase the meaning of the musical experience, but it does not replace for the experiences of meaning at a non-verbal level.

An intersubjective perspective on music therapy acknowledges the therapeutic relationship as a frame and a relational possibility in and of itself for development and change. Two different inner worlds meet within the intersubjective frame of mutual regulation and interaction through music. The intersubjective experiences exceed each person's subjective state of mind. There is a fusion of horizons. Hence, intersubjectivity includes an intentional use of the musical relationship in itself.

In short, intersubjective participation is a developmental process from regulation to a reflecting function (mentalization). Intersubjectivity concerns people making a special kind of mental connection with their immediate and subjective experience at the forefront. It includes a kind of mental flow, an implicit and procedural knowing that has experience, body and affects in the here-and-now at its very core. The present intersubjectivity, which has modern developmentally informed psychology as its basis, presents itself in practice through four *interaction formats* (Hansen, 2012, p. 85-86):

> *Primary intersubjectivity* is the immediate sense of joint attention and emotional synchronization and regulation.

Intersubjectivity emerges through mutual affective exchange including imitation, and through crossmodal exchange of form and contours in a face-to-face contact within a time frame (Trevarthen, 1980).

Secondary intersubjectivity is joint attention linked to a focus or object outside oneself, while realizing both the interaction itself and an awareness of being an active co-creator of one's own and another's intra- and interpersonal worlds. Social referring and sharing of affects are linked to a shared and joint focus outside oneself (Stern, 1985; Trevarthen & Hubley, 1978).

Tertiary intersubjectivity is communication through symbols, verbal exchange, and narratives, including integration of affects (Bråten, 2007). Play is an important part of this type of intersubjective exchange.

Tertiary intersubjectivity of second order (Bråten, 2007) is about the ability to attribute feelings, intentions, and thoughts both to oneself and to others (mentalization). In other words, this is a perspective on a "mental life" that creates preconditions for reflecting and thinking about oneself and others beyond the here-and-now. This format includes the ability to integrate experiences into autobiographical narratives as well.

All these formats of intersubjective participation are included in the therapeutic process and create the frame for the development and emergence of something new, that is, new subjective experiences and patterns of relating. It is primarily intersubjective exchange that creates the basis for the development of subjectivity, coherence, creation of meaning, possibilities of action, and language.

Microprocesses are of vital importance to grasp basic characteristics in an intersubjective process. These include movements, facial expressions, timing, rhythm, tempo, and intensity from moment to moment in the here-and-now (Johns & Svendsen, 2012; Stern, 2004). These elements influence subjective experience while also shaping the intersubjective contact through direct experiences. Such a perspective presupposes attentional presence and emotional availability. Microprocesses are linked to Stern's definition of experience of the present moment as "our microscope for viewing how change comes about" (2004, p. xix). These important moments are often unspoken and relational, and they happen in a moment. In music therapy, microanalyses are mainly exploratory rather than theory-driven, and studies examine naturalistic rather than laboratory settings. In the last decade, phenomenological and ethnographic methodologies of interpretivist microanalyses in music therapy have developed (Trondalen & Wosch, In press; Wosch & Wigram, 2007).

Intersubjective moments—present musical moments—involve microprocesses. However, a musical moment (in musical time) may last several seconds. It might not be too important to count seconds when we are talking about a moving-along process in music therapy, but it is interesting to compare microanalyses of musical moments in music therapy to Stern's "moment of meeting." Moments of meeting, objectively lasting from 1 to 10 seconds with a median of 3 to 4 seconds, can be experienced as an "uninterrupted *now*" (Stern, 2004).

Microanalysis of "significant moments" of two improvisations in music therapy identified a mean of 28.5 seconds (Trondalen, 2004a, 2005b). Ansdell, Davidson, Magee, Meehan, and Procter (2010) identified shared phrases ranging from 8 to 35 seconds, with a median of 13.5. What stands out as crucial to me is that these moments of moving along together in the music *are* of limited duration. They are experienced as *condensed periods or events* in which something changes within the musical relationship. The musical process involved temporal and spatial dimensions (Ansdell et al., 2010; Trondalen, 2004a). The time phrase in music therapy may be similar to what Stern (2004) calls extended present moments, or they may relate to Malloch's (1999) "stanzas of musical activity," suggesting an average of 30 seconds. These microprocesses are a cornerstone in intersubjective exchange, just as in music therapy, as they form the basis for development of subjectivity, togetherness, creation of meaning, and possibilities of actions and language.

17

Chapter 3

Development As A Dialogical Continuum

Stern (1985, 2000), a psychoanalyst and infant researcher, has made important contributions to our thinking about an individual's ability to interact socially, especially through his focus on microprocesses and his descriptions of the development of senses of self, not least in therapy processes. Stern proposed a bridge between psychoanalysis and modern developmental psychology, describing interpersonal and intrapsychic processes in a systemic perspective. He suggested that the way in which a human being experiences oneself and being with others represents an organizing principle of all human events. In addition, Stern linked the knowledge gained through non-verbal experiences to the ways in which these experiences are interweaved in a continuum of development.

Stern (2000) suggested a layered model of development, which is *not* limited to the first years of a person's life. On the contrary, it encompasses a *lifelong* accumulation of senses of self, socio-affective competencies, and ways of being with others. Stern combined the "clinical" and the "observed" infant within a lifelong process of self-development. He posited that the individual is a competent person who influences her or his surroundings via a dialogical mode of interaction from the very beginning. Stern's subjectively experiencing infant model proposed that the development of the individual moves through adulthood through a series of overlapping and inter-dependent layers.

The layered model of development maintains that self-other differentiation is in place and in process virtually from the beginning of a person's life, rather than being a phase-limited undertaking (Piaget, 1954). Therefore, Stern (2000, p. xiii) stated, "The infant's major developmental task is the opposite one, the creation of ties with others—that is, increasing relatedness." As time passes, these layers become increasingly interpersonally sophisticated, as they remain active and interact dynamically with each other over one's life span.

The model proposes a continuous construction process, in which subjectivity and intersubjectivity develop in parallel and mutually influence one another. As previously stated, it includes a procedural, dialogical construction process with feelings as the primary agent. Meaning and coherence are therefore constituted through an active co-creation and interplay with other fellow beings, including intersubjective sharing and interaction (Bråten, 1998; Trevarthen, 1999). For an illustration of the different senses of self and the equivalent domains, see Stern (2000, Figure 2.2, p. xxv).

Stern's layered model includes four leaps in the development of senses of self, and each leap is understood as a *domain of relatedness.* The different *senses of self* emerge within these domains of relatedness. The first two domains involve bodily affective interplay. The first domain includes the sense of an emergent self, the sense of a core self, and the sense of a core self with another. The second domain is equivalent to the sense of an intersubjective self. The third and fourth domains, which develop as the child learns to speak, are the verbal self and the narrative self (selves). These domains of relatedness emerge in succession and comprise a self-organizing principle of lived experiences:

> No emerging domain disappears; each remains active and interacts dynamically with each other. In fact, each domain facilitates the emergence of the ones that follow. In this way, all senses of self, all socioaffective competencies, and all ways-of-being-with-others remain with us throughout the life span. (Stern, 2000, p. xii)

These domains of relatedness, embedding the different senses of self, are active and organize one's experiences throughout life. Events that influence these domains may arise at any time of life, including adulthood, and introduce vulnerabilities. Senses of self are active and continuously developing during a lifespan. This is opposed to the therapeutic approach of searching for a certain point in time, or one specific experience, as the starting point for mental problems and challenges. The therapist should understand the client based on her or his relating experiences and systemic pattern of interplay. Thus, a broad description of the person's characteristics and challenges is necessary to understand a person based on her or his personal subjectivity and life history.

Stern is aware that his model can never be more than a hypothetical way of understanding the individual, since it is not possible to render a child's experience of being in the world. Such a view, however, does contrast with earlier assumptions regarding the child as a passive recipient of impressions from the environment. At a meta-psychological level, this relational turn means that drives (Freud, 1920) change places with emotions and affects as the primary forces of mental development.

Stern's subjectively experiencing infant involves layers of *senses of self* that emerge within different domains of relatedness. As new capacities emerge, the senses of self are reorganized to form organizing subjective perspectives on self and others. Different senses of self emerge in quantum leaps. The primary intersubjectivity, the onset, starts at the beginning of life, as does the sense of an emergent self, core self, and core-self-with-another (Stern, 2000, p. xxii).

A *sense of an emergent self* includes the ways in which the individual is aware of and perceives an organization of different modes of bodily sensing. The emergent self connects to the physical regulation and stabilization of the senses. Crossmodal perception (amodal and holistic sensing) and interaction with a significant other (for example, the mother) supplies the basis for a coherent of sense of self (Meltzoff & Borton, 1979; Stern, 2010). Global qualities such as form, intensity, movement, and rhythm are building blocks of the emergent self. Studies show that the individual can recognize accordance between time and intensity, as well as auditory, visual, and tactile patterns of relating. Crossmodal perception helps the person to integrate and store different senses of experience and to integrate the different experiences of self and others.

The following example is drawn from expressive music therapy. A music therapist was working with elderly people who were struggling with confusion and restlessness; many of them had dementia. A male client, Hans, seemed upset because of an unforeseen event, unpredictability, or a lack of coherence between his personal needs and reality. The music therapist sat down at his bedside and started to sing a folk tune to calm the elderly and restless client while stroking his hand. The music therapist used her voice and gentle touch while attuning to the client through the form, rhythm, and intensity of the folk song. The man became calm and, a short time later, quietly fell asleep. The gentle touch and the music therapist's voice, seemed to lead to an activation curve, a contour similar to a vitality feeling of fading, and consequently to relaxation. These senses may be coded as crossmodal perception and be experienced as an emergence of the self. In this setting, music and a gentle hand touch without words facilitated a transition from restlessness to a relaxed state of mind.

Another example comes from receptive music therapy. Sveinung, age 75, had experienced a stroke in his left hemisphere and was hospitalized. He felt upset and greatly struggled to express himself. His anxiety and claustrophobia appeared with full strength during the night. The music therapist, knowing that Sveinung loved music, made a CD containing some of his favorite songs. He put a small CD player at his bedside and could operate the music himself when he wanted, even overnight. The man used the music actively to calm himself, trusting that it could give some comfort during his anxiety attacks and offer him some freedom when claustrophobia threatened him. When Sveinung regained some of his speech, he told the music therapist that the music had indeed helped him through those long nights. When language and one's bodily perception change radically in a moment, movement and rhythm are at risk. The person's inner life is trapped inside as communication with the surroundings falls apart. Sveinung, used music, carefully selected by another person who tried to understand his despair, to integrate and store senses of experiences. He seemed to allow the music to take over and organize his inner chaos in a way that could give him some comfort. Hence, the musical experiences supported his regulation of inner intensity and regulation toward a more coherent sense of self.

The *sense of a core self* is another experiential sense. The individual is an active if insufficient partner in face-to-face dialogues through turn taking, with its inherent exchange of eye contact, movement, and vocalizing. The interplay is based on themes with variations, repetitions, and exaggerations. The first mutually shared play includes playing with forms of vitality where co-creation in the here-and-now, together with variations in intensity, creates excitement and shared joy. Meaning and coherence link to experience and events. This means that the individual is organizing experiences from interactions in episodic memory. Stern (2000, p. 94) described episodic memories with reference to Tulving (1972) as "memory for real-life experiences occurring in real time." These episodes of real life experiences range from actual life events, such as playing a drum in music therapy, to more psychologically informed memories. An example of the latter would be what one client experienced (felt sad) when a nurse at an inpatient unit told the client that a music therapy session had been cancelled. Episodic memory means being able to include actions, perceptions, and affects as the main ingredients or attributes of a remembered episode. When the person recognizes repeated patterns and events across differences, then three self-invariants are created: self-agency, self-coherence, and self-continuity (Stern, 2000, p. xix).

Sara, age 14, was an inpatient at a child psychiatric unit because she had stopped taking (Trondalen, 2001). During the previous few years, she had been badly abused and bullied, especially by fellow pupils (for example, by having sand forced down her throat). It was difficult to communicate with Sara on a daily basis, and music therapy aimed at supporting her recovery of verbal language. During her music therapy program, Sara attended 32 music therapy sessions.

The music therapy sessions included a variety of impro-visational activities. In the second-last session, Sara performed music on birdcalls, she played a variety of instruments, and we danced together. Sara had performed real-life experiences ranging from actual life events, such as playing a drum in music therapy, to more psychologically informed memories where she could express how it felt for her when she played. As we were about to do our farewell song, Sara suddenly looked at me and whispered very determinedly, "Kinder Surprise" (that is a chocolate egg that contains a toy inside a plastic shell). "Do you want a Kinder Surprise?" I asked. She nodded. I told her that she had to walk down to the unit and tell the staff what she wanted. After concluding the session, we proceeded to the ward together. Sara knocked on the door to the ward office and stated with a firm voice, "Here I am and I want Kinder Surprise." She indeed got what she wanted.

In this session, Sara moved from silence to saying aloud what she wanted. She had presented herself through a variety of participating actions in music therapy, performing self-agency non-verbally. In this case, the voice became an influential way of opening an important channel of communication and a very powerful gesture to herself and others as she resumed her audible behavior. She performed self-agency (a self-invariant of a sense of a core self), telling what she wanted and taking action to get a Kinder Surprise. I assume that this was possible due to our previous musical playing and exploration, which afforded her with possibilities to use her whispering voice actively and to take actions and decide for herself, both non-verbally and through bodily participation.

Leon, a single 27-year-old man, was a musician and composer who struggled with the frequent occurrence of negative thoughts. He hoped that music listening through GIM sessions (in a private music therapy practice) would help him to understand some of the mechanisms underlying his negative and destructive behaviors, and that eventually this experience would support him in his daily life as a performer and composer. His receptive music therapy engagement included five individual GIM sessions over two months.

In session four, during the music program *Inner Odyssey* (Bonny, 1989, as cited in Grocke, 2002a), Leon met for the first time with a "sensitive swan bowing its head." In the pre-conversation at the start of the final session, Leon talked about being both optimistic and worried at the same time. The music program selected was *Mostly Bach,* with a total length of 45 minutes and 3 seconds (Bonny, 1977, as cited in Grocke, 2002a). During *#1 Bach: Passacaglia and Fugue in C minor*, Leon moved from bathing in a dark sea with nobody around to being transformed into a flying swan. He felt at home in the air and arrived at the infinite ocean. After the listening experience, Leon made a drawing that he titled "The arrival at the infinite ocean." In his verbal communication after the journey, Leon said that his experience with the swan was powerful. He felt safe and wanted to bring "the feeling of safety within eternity" into his daily life.

24

During this GIM journey, Leon experienced the music in the here-and-now (at a non-verbal level), while also exploring a sense of a core self (self-coherence), through his feeling of being transformed into the swan. To him, the swan meant neither life nor death; it was between two worlds. "The swan is immortal," he said. The freedom to act and the power of freedom were essential for Leon, as he longed for musical creativity and a deepening of his spirituality as a human spirit. From a musical point of view, the *Passacaglia and Fugue* established a power of dynamics, through its gradually accumulating volume and complexity (Bruscia, 2014b; Grocke, 2002a). The essential quality was in the repetition, providing strong structure to the work. There are contrasts between the full texture in the orchestra and softer, lighter variations. Leon connected to the music, saying, "I have realized how important feelings are, as indeed not everything is related to cognition." I believe that a new relational experience through music supported a sense of a core self and emotional coherence and meaning, which in turn eventually supported expressiveness of feeling. The power of freedom, which was central to Leon as he longed for musical creativity and a deepening of his spirituality, can be a way of performing self-continuity.

The *sense of a core self with another* includes sharing motives and intentions with another. Its self-invariants of experience are self-with-a-self-regulating-another, self-resonating-with-another, and self-in-the-presence-of-another (Stern, 2000). To create and recognize these invariants, the individual benefits from a self-regulating other (Tronick, 1989), that is, a person who is emotionally aware, available, and capable of picking up and regulating the interaction in a sensitive way, in accordance with the individual's shifts in emotions. If the person does not experience sensitive regulation, that person develops different means of self-regulation. Central elements within the sense of a core self with another are face-to-face interaction and the experience of being able to influence.

Lisa, age 25 and suffering from an eating disorder, was participating in expressive music therapy in an individual outpatient setting. An experienced pianist, she loved playing the grand piano. In the sixth of ten sessions, she and I improvised on two grand pianos for 12 minutes. The client set the tone as she introduced a Spanish mode with the harmonic progression of D minor, C major, B♭ major and A major[7] in repetition. The music therapist and client improvised in different tempi, intensity, and volume, responding to each other's musical initiatives. Sometimes the musical improvisation grew into a crescendo. At other times, it nearly faded away, but then emerged again. After about 10 minutes of playing, the music turned into a meditative vocal duet in the *piano* to *mezzo piano* loudness range. The harmonies on the piano accompanied the ebb and flow in the vocalizations. We were sometimes looking at each other, sometimes playing with our eyes closed.

In the verbal conversation afterwards, Lisa said she was amazed about the mutual adjustment process that took place through our musical exploration and the dynamic shifts in the music. She experienced "the feeling of mastering" when playing with another person who was playing the same instrument (sense of a core self). "I have never played like this before," she said. Lisa obviously enjoyed the joint improvisation, which enabled her to explore self-regulation in a controlled way together with the music therapist. Self-regulation is the issue at stake when one is having difficulty controlling one's emotions or eating. The experience of mutual influence and self-regulation through a music improvisation was a powerful experience for her.

Sigrid, age 22, attended receptive music therapy, GIM sessions. She was a music student, always aiming toward perfection on her instrument. She felt that the exercises and pressure to achieve perfection were draining, physically as well as mentally. In session five, the last in the music therapy process, Sigrid listened to the music program *Consoling* (Bruscia & Grocke, 2002; Meadows, 2010). During *#1 Sibelius: Swan of Tuonela*, the following dialogue took place (my comments are in italics):

> The music is far away—something is going to happen—
> [*Can you say more?*]—the music is building up some
> expectations—[*Tell me more*]—the music just goes on—
> [*Allow the music to lead you*]—(Sigrid begins to cry) [*What
> are you aware of?*]—I miss him (i.e., her boyfriend). (The
> music shifts to the Andantino of Debussy's String Quartet).

[*Would you like to invite him into the music?*]—(smiling)
now we are playing together—[*Allow yourself to stay with
him in the music*]—we are following the music together.

Sigrid greatly enjoyed the experience of inviting her boyfriend
into her GIM journey. The music therapist acted as a self-regulating
other, picking up and regulating the conversation in a sensitive way,
in accordance with Sigrid's shifts in emotions. Sigrid enjoyed the
experience of playing music together with her boyfriend, which may
have been one way for her to sense her core self with another.

The *sense of an intersubjective self* (emerging from 9 months) is
another experiential sense related to a new domain, the domain of an
intersubjective self. It is following the first, which included the sense
of an emergent self, the sense of a core self, and the sense of a core
self with another. Core elements in the second domain are intentions,
feelings, and the sharing of joint attention outside oneself. The
individual can share joint attention, such as by 'playing' on an
instrument. The person can share inner states of mind and feelings
by means of an object (instrument) outside herself or himself (Stern,
2000; Trevarthen, 1980). Stern (1984) suggested the term *affect
attunement* to clarify such an emotional exchange within the frame of
intersubjectivity. Affect attunement is the sharing of inner feeling
states. In such a sharing, a matching takes place, or a crossmodal way
of relating (as the exploration of the interplay may occur across
different modalities, which still relate to each other). The key here is
how the interaction moves along, rather than merely the themes or
the musical actions per se (Trondalen & Skårderud, 2007). Essential
elements in such an experience are timing, intensity, and form, in
addition to motion, and rhythm.

Silje, age 12, was an inpatient at a child psychiatric center. She
was very capable of expressing herself in words, but connecting to—
and expressing—emotions was scary and difficult. She was a good
piano player. In the second out of nine music therapy sessions, Silje
chose to express herself through different birdcalls while I played the
piano. We then played a duet on the piano while we explored the
theme of 'being together'. Silje played the treble and I played the bass.
Improvisation on chime bars organized in a pentatonic scale (with

27

me accompanying on piano) followed, and then a duet on the hand drums and a final improvisation on with Silje playing maracas and me at the piano. During the last improvisation, Silje smiled for the very first time in the session. She seemed to especially enjoy the last activity. "This is different," she said. "I have never used music like we are doing here."

In all the musical activities, a rhythmical matching and attunement were taking place. Timing and exploration of intensity and form were evident throughout the improvisational explorations. Silje explored the musical relationship in a sensitive and interested way. In the end of the session, she said, "Music therapy is more difficult and more demanding than 'usual' therapy." "Why is that so?" I asked. "Because you cannot hide within the music, and because you give more of yourself in the music making," she explained. Silje had explored a sense of an intersubjective self.

A group of young people, age 18 to 25, was participating in a music therapy workshop as a part of a leadership program. Receptive music therapy offered self-experience and personal development through music listening experiences. In one session, the eight participants laid on the floor, on their backs, with their heads facing the center of the circle. They listened to Sting's music, "How Fragile We Are", from the album *Nothing like the Sun* (1987; 3 minutes 54 seconds).

Before the actual listening, the music therapist offered an autogenic form of relaxation. The participants were then invited to report their experiences to the group during the music listening while creating a story together. At one point, two of the participants started to talk at the same time. I noticed that they opened their eyes simultaneously and broke into smiles before closing their eyes again and joining the music journey. In the verbal processing afterwards, the two youngsters investigated this experience: "Do you remember when we both started talking at the same time?" Again, they smiled at each other, as they both recognized this joint, shared experience. Emotional and mental processes had been involved. The music listening experience obviously created a special connection (sense of an intersubjective self) between the two of them; something had changed in their relationship.

28

The last two domains include the *verbal self* (emerging between age 18 and 36 months) and the *narrative self* (from 36 months onward). These domains embrace symbols and self-narratives. On one hand, using words represents a new opportunity to develop, create, and experience stories and narratives about oneself. On the other hand, using words reduces the opportunity to share and describe the immediate sensation of the lived experience, because the close immediacy of the sensed and experienced disappears in the distance created by words. Stern (2000, p. 162) explained:

> But in fact language is a double-edged sword. It also makes some parts of our experience less shareable with ourselves and others. It drives a wedge between two simultaneous forms of interpersonal experience: as it is lived and as it is verbally represented.

These domains of relating include dialogue and negotiation of the lived world. A mutual process of interaction embraces an exploration of symbols and narratives. The idiosyncratic single narrative is different from person to person. The focus is on the lived experience rather than the historical fact.

The *verbal self* links to co-creating within a shared world of experiences. The participants negotiate a final version of a highly idiosyncratic story, which has "an uncertain relationship with the historical truth" (Stern, 2000, p. xxv). It has the lived experience of co-creation at its very core. Through dialogue and negotiations, the shared life world develops on the basis of concrete actions, symbolic images, and play.

Charlotte, age 31, was a highly qualified university student suffering from anorexia nervosa. This was her fourth music therapy session, which turned out to be her last as she was hospitalized due to the severity of her illness shortly afterwards. During this expressive music therapy session, she was anxious about her upcoming exams, which included many diagnostic terms in Latin. We created an improvisation consisting of the different diagnostic terms she had to learn by heart. The musical form was rap. In this way, we addressed her need for repetition and had fun at the same time, which affected her body in a positive way. When summing up the session, Charlotte wrote, "Charlovotti."

In music therapy, images and words emerged during the shared but not identical experience of the improvised rap. Fragments and short sentences of diagnostic terms and feelings were explored in a funny way and were given a musical form in the context. At a clinical level, the rap included important emotional values and events in the client's life as she was preparing for her exams. The rhythm provided Charlotte's verbal self with an audible structure. The rap became a sound file of Charlotte's inner life in the here-and-now.

We can also give an example from receptive music therapy. Ann was a successful female executive in her mid-thirties, working in an international business firm. She attended music therapy because Ann and her superior had agreed that unresolved issues in Ann's life seemed to hinder her work performance. The client attended music therapy for five sessions over a four-month period. The length of music therapy was based on a plan for focused, and time-limited (Peterlin & Sloves, 1985; Proskauer, 1971) individual GIM. Ann came to music therapy with a clear mission: "I want to explore my rucksack of sadness" (Trondalen, 2009–2010), she said. Ann's rucksack in life was heavy, metaphorically speaking.

The third session provided a turning point. She listened to the program *Nurturing (Modified)* (Bonny, 1978, in Bruscia & Grocke, 2002, Appendix B). Ann had images of dark skies, wonderful nature, and old furniture. She met with her deceased dad and grandma, and she returned to the old church and her dad's funeral. The client reminisced about old times while imagining people playing the music. Her vision of nature was stunning. Ann made a drawing, a mandala of "the place," seen through the porthole of a ship passing by.

Ann's lived experience, images, analogies to her personal life, and concrete actions were explored and co-created within a relational framework. The verbal dialogue allowed for a procedural understanding of the relationship between the musical journey itself and its interpretations or representations of the experience, in relation to an anticipated future. Such a relational mode of surrender (Blom, 2014) into intersubjectivity permits exploration of a transformative and transpersonal experience including implicit (non-verbal) relational knowing and intersubjective consciousness. During the last session, Ann commented that music had worked, but she did not know why. Something had happened.

The sense of a *narrative self* embraces symbols and self-narratives as a basis for co-creation of a personal narrative. The stories and narratives are idiosyncratic as they will differ from one individual to another. The client's lived history is at the very core of the narrative. Personal experiences are the basis for the creation of the narrative self, which is constructivist in its essence.

We can return to Sara, the 14-year-old girl in the psychiatric unit, for another example of expressive music therapy. After three months of her music therapy process, Sara fetched two maracas and looked at me excitingly as she played a rhythmical pattern. I immediately repeated her rhythmical figure with chords at the piano and sang, "Sara can play maracas." The rest of the song described in concrete terms Sara's active participation in the sessions. The improvised song became a special one to her, an "identity-song." In the actual setting, music and words (songwriting) emerged during a shared but not identical experience of improvisation. Sentences and fragments were elaborated upon and given a musical form. The lyrics included important emotional highlights, values, and events in Sara's life. Melody and chords provided the personal narrative with an audible structure and story line. The song become a soundtrack of her life as well.

Lars, a man in his thirties, attended 17 individual sessions of GIM over a period of 13 months. Lars needed a long time to find words that expressed his feelings satisfactorily. He tended to spend his energy unevenly during his daily life and to take on too large a workload. As a result, he spent many days with a burned-out and exhausted feeling and struggled with dark thoughts (Trondalen, 2010). Session 14 turned out to be of particular importance to Lars, like a sort of hero's journey. The music program was *Mythic Journey* (as cited in Bruscia & Grocke, 2002, Appendix F). The journey included phases parallel to the hero's journey (Clark, 1995, 2002). During the oboe concerto, waves of colors touched the flute (Lars's personal instrument). The flute suddenly stood up, surrounded by the colors. Then client found himself inside a large glass square. He called it exciting and described a feeling of a significant moment (the hero's call to adventure). The colors started to move, and Lars walked over and took the flute. Everything was overwhelming, but he took his time ("crossing the threshold" in the hero's journey). The world and the colors then split up. He was left with the flute and the darkness expanded ("for trails and task" in the journey). In the end, the client then saw a great light, left the enormous room and returned on his way back home ("reward"). Lars felt that he had not yet arrived but had come back to reality ("return"), where he was met by several voices ("carries his secret with him inside").

During the GIM experience, Lars embraced different images and symbols, which he brought into his daily life. The GIM session, which incorporated music listening, relaxation, drawing, and verbal conversation, strengthened and supported personal and professional development and enhanced a coherent sense of a narrative self. Such a development within this domain of relating deals with the feeling of being in synchronization with the therapist, the music, and the experience of being able to influence within the music listening journey. Accordingly, meaning and sense of coherence connect to action and lived experience. The client later stated that his hero's journey reappeared in his mind's eye while he was traveling in his car. Lars described it as a strengthening and important experience.

Comments on Stern's Developmental Model

The present text suggests an intersubjective perspective on relational music therapy, with references to different theorists. One cornerstone of prior research, though, is the work of Daniel Stern (2000), particularly his focus on the subjectively experiencing infant. Stern's model has faced criticism from several perspectives, including primarily a social-constructionist point of view (Cushman, 1991), as well as critical comments regarding observations on infants' relevance for psychoanalysis (Wolff, 1996, Mills, 2005). Stern (2000) has responded to this type of criticism. Other commenters have remained reflective towards such a type of criticism (Hannibal, 2000; Johnsen, Sundet, & Thorsteinsson, 2000). In the present text, I will primarily focus on the criticism surrounding the infant's development of the self as a universal size, including some reflections on the validity of Stern's hypotheses.

Stern's (2000) concern was the development of different senses of self to understand the clinical and the observed infant. Such a way of looking at reality is not reality itself; it is a construction. The social-constructionist critique points out that Stern does not relate to self-development as socially constructed, that is, depending on historical, cultural, and contextual factors. The individual is characterized and created by the local culture in which he lives, Cushman (1991) argued. This means that the self also serves as a mirror of the era and the culture that the community is promoting at a certain point of time. Self-development is real, but it cannot be connected with universal aspects of the self. Cushman also claimed that Stern over-interpreted his data, arguing that the data appeared to be more positivistic than phenomenological, the latter being Stern's basis. Such criticism is particular related to the development of domains of the self. For example, the critique pointed out that the various aspects of sense of a core self (agent status, coherence, continuity and affectivity, that is, invariant quantities of senses of self) belong to the adult world, where mastery and narratives of their own stories are linked to group or other social affiliation. In this context, Cushman claimed, possessing such aspects of the core self means a belonging to a white American middle class culture. Also in relation to affectivity and language, Cushman criticized Stern for making development an innate and universal phenomenon, which is not adequately contextualized.

Language enables the sharing and negotiation of meaning, but at the same time, such explicit verbalization involves a removal from the immediate sharing of meaning at a non-verbal level. Such a view can be perceived as idyllic, as understanding seems to be based on the perception of an immediate connection between the non-verbal individual and nature, as a normal condition. Cushman (1991, p. 216) said, "This argument contains a kind of 'noble savage' view of the infant's development."

Another reflection is related to that old dualism, the split between nature and culture (Johnsen et al., 2000). Such a split can easily lead to the assumption that mothers and fathers are somehow guilty if the dialogue between the individual and the caregiver does not develop in a good way. Accordingly, cultural and social factors are marginalized. I think this point is worth taking into account both theoretically and in music therapy practice. Music therapy always takes place in a cultural and social context. Music improvisations and music listening take place on the basis of social (including music culture), psychological, and biological factors. Therapist, client, and context are therefore influencing these improvisations and music listening experiences in music therapy in a broad sense. Stern (2000) responded to the social-constructionist critique by agreeing that it is important to be critical of influence from the surrounding culture, for political and scientific reasons. However, he pointed out, that *"The Interpersonal World of The Infant* is primarily about the process whereby social contexts are enacted so as to shape people's behavior, their inner worlds, and their relationships" (Stern, 2000, pp. xxvi-xxvii).

Stern went on to say that culture can be viewed from the outside, or understood as micro-cultures within a family. In a small cultural unity that a close relationship constitutes, only a certain number of variables, such as facial expressions, gazes, and vocalizations, are needed to support early socio-cultural contextualization. On the one hand, Stern recognized that only through a culture with certain basic assumptions (white, middle- and upper-class society in the mid-twentieth century) that 'his' individuals develop. On the other hand, Stern asserted that at times there appears to be an innate preference, tendency, capacity, or timing of appearance. With regard to the term *pre-designed*, he clarified as follows:

> But what I mean by predesigned is that there is an innate human capacity to feel the effortful, temporal form of another's action. For example, the aforementioned findings regarding mirror neurons and adaptive oscillators supply a biologically based mechanism for the human capacity to feel another's action. The fact that this capacity can take different cultural forms does not make the capacity less innate; it only suggests how different cultures might use it. (Stern, 2000, p. xxviii).

34

Such a view does not impair such a capacity, but it will unfold differently due to the conditions and cultures it encounters. It does not alter the innate phenomenon, but provides slightly different results as to how the different cultures will relate to and use this capacity. In short, the cultural element will act as a developmental variable itself.

Stern has been criticized for over-interpreting his data as he connects it to theory and draws conclusions. Stern admitted the challenge of "drawing inferences or hypotheses from the objective constraints. There is no way that inferences about another's subjective experience can escape at least some contamination from the experiences and beliefs of the person doing the inferring" (2000, p. xxxi). Stern's hypothesis formation, he said, arose from the totality of his "emphatic, accumulated understanding of normal human behavior" (p. xxxi), of which his knowledge gained from patients is only a small part. The basis of his interpretation and hypothesizing did not rest on the tenets of any preexisting theory; rather, a broadly inclusive approach, taking into account the totality of human experience, underpinned the process of inference making while skirting the circularity scientifically as far as possible. Using a broadly inclusive approach, while suggesting a model of the development of senses of self, also seems to embrace a link between the individual and the society—in a broad sense. This, he claims, to have done without focusing on theories of adult psychopathology.

In relation to the present text, I find Stern's elucidation of his method helpful by way of clarification. I agree with others who have reflected upon and validated the significance of Stern's contribution to the understanding of development of self (Hannibal, 2000; Hansen, 2012). Some critics seem not so occupied with the influential shift from a directed operation to a relational theoretical understanding of the development. In Stern's dialogical model (2000), the relational perspective accounts for the driving forces of development of self and the relationship to intimate others. This includes the development of the individual's representations, the individual's biological constitution, and the caregiver's relationship to culture at a micro and macro level.

The importance of the innate capacity to develop senses of

oneself within a relationship, and its relevance for non-verbal processes in music therapy, triggered my interest in Stern's model from the beginning. It resonated intuitively with my own personal experience of relationships inside a music therapy setting, and in life in general. In Stern's dialogical model, I found some useful concepts by which to explore experiences within music therapy processes. Stern identified self-experiences and interaction as primary foundations of a relationship, which easily transferred to explorations of the musical relationship. Terms like mutual influence and regulation, self with others, social referencing (Emde & Sorce, 1983), intersubjectivity, and the negotiation of meaning contributing to new narratives felt close to my reality as a music therapist (Trondalen, 2004a). To me, these were phenomenal terms linked closely to lived musical experiences in expressive and receptive music therapy.

Stern's perspective (2000) is constructivist in nature. Nevertheless, his theoretical framework is founded on empirical research on typically developing infants. Music therapy practice includes clients at all ages and stages of life, with the client(s) and therapist(s) taking on various roles. To me, there is no contradiction between possible mechanisms of universality, which offer an *innate* preference or timing in relation to a phenomenon, as long as it connects to and interprets the actual cultural *context*. In other words, I appreciate a reflexive attitude towards the tension between universals and historical context in a music therapy setting. The theoretical basis is also evident as to how to analyze and interpret a music therapy process, addressing musical and interpersonal perspectives at a micro level as well (Trondalen & Wosch, In press,). An intersubjective perspective on relational music therapy highlights the therapeutic relationship established through music, which is interactive in nature. From an analytical point of view, a contextual view is important but does not reduce the impact of the implicit relating experiences per se.

To describe free-flowing affects, Stern uses some musical terminology, such as crescendo, diminuendo, and sostenuto. This does not imply that Stern is talking directly about how the music unfolds in, for example, a play song, an improvisation, or a listening procedure. Music therapists have argued that mother-infant interaction and music improvisation are not equivalent (Rolvsjord, 1996; Tønsberg & Hauge, 1996). They can, however, be seen as parallel and complementary processes (Johns, 1993; Smeijsters, 2012).

The affective dialogue and regulation of affects are of vital importance in early communication and in life in general. Feelings, emotions, and affects follow us throughout our life span. They do not disappear when language and symbolic thinking emerge. Affective turn taking and regulation are building blocks for verbalized dialogue as one grows up. A constant negotiation process constitutes meaning, whether the situation is physical or mental in nature, involving the relationship itself or content at a more semantic level. Knowledge of others and of oneself emerges within the contextual relationship. When the overall focus is on creating meaning, actions, feelings, and cognition appear as integrated and not divided into different categories.

Music therapy fits into a broader context than a dual relationship or a group setting within inpatient care. Everybody belongs to a wider environment, a contextual and ecological system. Sometimes music therapy is performed within an inpatient setting (Trondalen, 2001); at other times, it takes place in community-based rehabilitation (Ansdell & DeNora, 2016; Jampel, 2011; Krüger, 2012). From a clinical point of view, it is important to support a transfer of the experiences from one part of the client's life to another. Whether the music therapy context is inpatient or community-based, it is equally important for a music therapist to be aware of and work through and in the context of a relationship.

Finally, however, the essence of this developmental process is the power of the mutual regulation process in itself. This process does not belong only to one context. It actually takes place within different contexts, regardless of the social culture.

Chapter 4

Implicit Relational Knowing

Music therapy offers relational experiences through music. These experiences sometimes prompt changes in the client's life, and even in the therapist's life as well. Relational experiences are non-verbal processes that involve implicit (non-verbal) relational knowing. Lyons-Ruth (1998) advocated that "something more" than interpretation is needed to bring about change in therapy. She hypothesized that one way to investigate change in therapy processes is to consider microprocesses within implicit relational knowing. To clarify, Lyons-Ruth described various ways in which non-verbal processes represent themselves. Two types of representational processes are involved in therapy, or in life in general: explicit and implicit knowledge.

Explicit knowledge is semantic and relies on its symbolic representation in language. Music, experiences, imagery, symbols, analogies, and metaphors are investigated through words (Bonde, 2000). Implicit knowledge, on the other hand, derives from a procedural and non-symbolic representation system that concerns itself with how to proceed or do things. Procedural knowledge includes rule-based representations and is different from verbalized knowledge or the dynamic unconscious. Procedural representations may never become symbolically coded.

Implicit knowledge involves two kinds of procedural representations: implicit generalized knowledge and implicit relational knowing (Lyons-Ruth, 1998). Examples of the first procedural representation—implicit generalized knowledge—are how to ride a bike or play an instrument. To do these things, one first "breaks the code," once and for all, after which one can specialize and improve but never loses the ability altogether. The second kind, implicit relational knowing, is more important in the present text, as it is connected to the feeling of *how to do things with others.* Examples from music therapy could include one's feeling of oneself and others while playing in a group improvisation with voice and instruments, or what one feels when describing one's emerging imagery to the music therapist in a GIM session.

Lyons-Ruth differentiated implicit relational knowing from other forms of procedural knowledge by highlighting the fact that it is as much affective and interactive as cognitive. It develops long before language and continuous to operate implicitly throughout one's life span:

> In our thinking, implicit relational knowing subsumes what has been termed internalized object relations. The older term, internalized object relations, has connotations of taking in from the outside, rather than of co-construction, and of taking in another person, rather than of representing a mutually constructed regulatory pattern (Tronick, 1989). The older term is also more identified with the literature on pathology rather than adaptive relatedness and is more often used to refer to past relationships and their activation in the transference rather than with more general representational models that are constantly accessed and updated in day-to-day encounters. (Lyons-Ruth, 1998, p. 285)

Transferred to a music therapy context, riding a bicycle could be likened to playing maracas. The rule-based procedural knowledge involved in both activities is generalized without necessarily being symbolically coded. However, playing the maracas *together* with another person activates implicit relational knowing that is affective and interactive in the here-and-now. Through playing and affect attunement, this form of joint playing can lead to musically related present moments or events that involve joint intersubjective recognition and give rise to a new implicit intersubjective understanding, or a new "way of being with the other."

Sometimes, change or new dimensions of experience arise without interpretation or verbal exploration, not least in music therapy. Tronick (1998) hypothesized a "dyadically expanded state of consciousness" to explore such a phenomenon. A dyadically expanded state of consciousness transcends language and exists in the procedural and emotional realms, not unlike musical experiences in music therapy. It emerges within an interpersonal non-verbal domain and includes intentions, affects, and intensity ("arousal"). Such a hypothesis understands the individual as a self-organizing system with its own state of consciousness and brain organization. This system can attain a more coherent and complex state when it encounters another self-organizing entity. Interpretation in a dyadically expanded state of consciousness builds on the client's and the therapist's previous experiences, not on a remembered narrative.

A dyadically expanded state of consciousness does not rely on interpretation in a traditional sense, nor is there a transference–countertransference process, as understood in psychoanalytic theory. It builds upon previous experiences between the client and the therapist, rather than on earlier and remembered narratives with significant others. "This field extends beyond the transference-countertransference domain to include authentic personal engagement and reasonably accurate sensings of each person's current way of being with" (Tronick, 1998, p. 285). The experience of mutual sharing of affects is central, as the implicit relational knowing of how to do things with intimate others dominates.

The hypothesis of a dyadically expanded state of consciousness is based on the *Mutual Regulation Model* (MRM; Tronick, 1989). Tronick's model provides a description of the "microregulatory social-emotional process of communication that generates (or fails to generate) dyadic intersubjective states of shared consciousness" (Tronick, 1998, p. 290). Interactive repairs follow interactive errors through a mutual adjustment process.

Tronick's philosophy can be used to explore the musical dialogue between the client and the music therapist in an optimistic way. That is, interactive "errors" in the music (for example, being out of tune) or challenges at a relational level (for example, feeling insecure with the other person's style of interaction) can be redefined as information that has the potential, not to halt or destroy the musical dialogue, but to maintain it. Thinking about interactive errors as information with this communicative potential could prevent the repetition of negative interactions. Thus, this whole process is seen as a natural part of being together in the musical communication. One way of describing this co-creation of meaning is that a mutual regulation process is based on a scaffolding process (Tronick, 1998; Emde, 1990). The music therapist is affectively responsive to the client in such a way as to support the individual's self-organization musically or relationally.

Central to such a mutual regulation model is the experience of mutual affective sharing in a "moment of meeting" (Stern, 1998, p. 305). At such a moment, a reorganization of both the client's and the therapist's mental organization occurs. In other words, the moment of meeting is the transactional event that reorganizes the client's implicit relational knowing through a reorganization of the intersubjective field between the client and the therapist . The experience is obviously unique to the two people. At the same time, there is a reconstruction of aspects connected to how it is to be with another. Such a view implies an expansion of the therapeutic setting, as the client is carrying this new reconstruction as a lived experience when encountering other people, which again is understood as an open system. Hence, *an expansion of the intersubjective field* (Tronick, 1998) *is a potent experience of change.*

We have met Sara (a 14-year-old girl in a child psychiatry unit) previously. The following example of expressive music therapy comes from the last week of her nine-month music therapy process (Trondalen, 2001). We had been playing on the piano together, and Sara had explored the whole piano with both hands, using black and white keys in expressive pitch variation in addition to short melodic lines. The session ended with us sitting beside each other after such an improvisation. I looked at her and said, "Now *you* can sing." After a brief silence, she nodded, grabbed the tape recorder (which was placed on the piano to audiotape the session) with both hands, and sang for the very first time with an emotional and clear voice, "It's time to say goodbye [...] we will meet again" (from Næss, 1981, p. 76; my translation). I supported her with my piano playing in C major. Sara moved from silence to being a singer within a moment.

The moment was a powerful one. As an answer to my invitation, which she had declined for nine months, she became visible to herself and me through music. As Sara sang, we joined each other in a way that we never had experienced before. We were attuned to—and in tune with—each other. Singing and playing together may have activated implicit relational knowing that was affective and interactive in the here-and-now. This form of joint playing seemed to involve intersubjective recognition and gave rise to a new implicit intersubjective understanding, or a new "way of being with the other." Sara followed this event by saying, "Here I am and I want Kinder Surprise," as described in the previous chapter, further expanding her intersubjective field. The experience of her singing aloud was unique to the two of us. At the same time, there was also a reconstruction of aspects connected to how it was to be with another. Sara experienced a new way of being with the music therapist. She then could carry this new reconstruction as a lived experience when meeting other people—an implicit relational knowing. Such a new encounter again can be understood as an open system.

When Sara left music therapy, I gave her a recording of music from the sessions, along with a kazoo. Both gifts carried the message of self-agency, co-creation, and continuity. Our joint music therapy narrative was symbolized in portable artefacts of relational living memories of music.

An example from receptive music therapy involves Julie, the 25-year-old university student and experienced piano player with anorexia nervosa. She arrived at her third outpatient music therapy session appearing extremely upset and distressed. I invited Julie to listen to an improvisation from her previous music therapy session through earphones while offering her blankets in which to wrap herself. This approach is called *self-listening*, in which "the client listens to a recording of his/her own improvisation, performance, or composition, to reflect upon oneself and the experience" (Bruscia 2014a, p. 139).

In the improvisation that Julie listened to, she played an African drum while the music therapist played the piano. Both were singing. During the self-listening experience, Julie apparently moved from chaos to order within less than three minutes. It seemed as if she connected to herself through music. Immediately after the self-listening experience, Julie said, "It is strange. During these two weeks, I feel I have known you for a long time. Everything is opening without doing anything to make it happen" (Trondalen, 2004a, p. 228).

I suggest that Julie's experience of the self-listening is an example of Tronick's "dyadically expanded state of consciousness." It seemed as if she experienced the improvisation in a procedural and emotional way. Such a dyadic state of consiousness emerges in the domain of interpersonal relating and includes intentions, affects, and levels of arousal. Julie explored rhythmic syncopation in her drum playing and singing, within a predictability consisting of repeated melodic chords (Dm-C-Bb-A7) (Trondalen, 2003). When the melodic line in the treble was steady during several bars, this emerged as a countermovement to the falling bass line in the piano. From a theoretical point of view, the syncopations could be seen as errors that were repaired and thus contributed to exploration of new forms of relating (Tronick, 1989), and to new ways of making music togehter. I propose that our two separated states of brain organization expanded into a more coherent and complex set of ways of being with one another throughout the playing.

Sometimes a musical moving-along process leads to a dyadic state of consciousness in which something changes. The unpredictable arising of an emergent property (Stern, 2004) brings about the shift. It has been prepared for during the musical moving-along process, perhaps by a shared intensity in the music or some lyrics put forward by the client or therapist. The union of musically informed elements results in the emergence of *now moments* and moments of meeting. "The essence of the now moment is that the established nature of the relationship and the usual way of being-with-each-other is implicitly called into question" (Stern, 2004, p. 166). Such a now moment occurred when I looked at Sara and said, "Now *you* can sing." Neither of us knew what was going to happen. More music? No visible or audible reaction? Similarly, what would Julie do immediately after the self-listening experience? She said, "Everything is opening without doing anything to make it happen." Both the therapist and the client shared an authentic personal experience, nicely adjusted to the situation (the now moment). The now moment was shaped by the local surroundings of the dyadic music therapy context, based on their previous musical sharing and unfolding in real time.

A now moment may or may not turn into a moment of meeting, which is a special form of present moment. "The moment of meeting is the present moment that resolves the crisis created by the now moment" (Stern, 2004, p. 168). It is one of the key events in bringing about change. The moment of meeting is the turning event that reorganizes implicit knowing by reorganizing the intersubjective field between the participants. Such a meeting is recognized by means of a sudden change from the usual. It is linked to the therapist's *immediate* response in the here-and-now. It is not about transference in a traditional way, but is linked to an authentic, sudden, and genuine response (Lyons-Ruth, 1998), which allows for a dyadic state of consciousness and for change. The intersubjective field expands in spite of the lack of linear and progression at the explicit and verbalized level.

The now moment(s) turned into a moment of meeting in the two examples presented in this chapter. The client and the therapist both knew they had directly experienced something of the other's experience. We created an implicit, intersubjective field that endured as a part of our shared musical story, our lived story together. The explicit content was temporarily put aside and out of mind, as we stayed focused on the temporal unfolding of feelings. A mutual sharing of affects provided the basis for Sara's vocal appearance and for Julie's experience of "everything is opening." These are both examples of a dyadically expanded state of consciousness. Both clients seemed to experience an implicit knowing of being alive and vital in the music therapist's presence. They also knew that the music therapist knew, which constitutes intersubjectivity. On this basis, I suggest that the experience of a dyadically expanded state of consciousness within music therapy, along with the subsequent expansion of the intersubjective field, counteracts existential loneliness.

Chapter 5

Vitality

Vitality is a basic key to understanding our feelings of being alive. It is a central and organizing quality and is basic to all affective communication, whether non-verbally or through language. The idea of vitality is a holistic way of thinking that provides the foundation for daily encounters with human behavior. It is a real human experience. We experience each other in terms of our vitality, as vitality connects to all our experiences within every modality and situation. Dynamic forms of vitality are the basis for our sense of being alive, inherent in all behavior.

The experience of vitality is an aspect of human experience that remains largely hidden in plain view. "We live impressions of vitality like we breathe air" (Stern, 2010, p. 3). Dynamic forms of vitality (previously called "vitality affects"; Stern, 1985) are events that manifest in different ways. They are demonstrated through movements, unfolding in a stretch of time. There is a temporal contour or time profile with a certain force and intentionality. "Therefore, starting with movement, we get five dynamic events linked together. These five theoretical events—movement, time, force, space and intention/ directionality—taken together give rise to the experience of vitality" (Stern, 2010, p. 4). Stern called force, time, space, and directionality the four daughters of movement.

Forms of vitality relate to *how* (the manner and the style) as opposed to the *what* or the *why*. Vitality concerns *how* we experience another, be it in daily life or through a music experience. Vitality can be treated as a mental creation, a subjective experience, and a phenomenal reality. It links to developmentally informed processes (Trevarthen, 1999) and neurobiology (Bråten, 2009; Siegel, 1999). Forms of vitality have a basis in physical actions and traceable mental operations. Vitality is a whole (a Gestalt), and it connects to all our experiences within every modality and situation.

Dynamic forms of vitality are inner experiences of being alive. They are always present and open to interpersonal relating. They are different from and do not comfortably fit into the traditional or Darwinian discrete categories of affects, such as anger, joy, sadness, happiness, disgust, surprise, interest, and perhaps shame, or their combinations (Stern, 2000).

Damasio (2000) investigated emotions as well, suggesting that emotions provide the platform or scaffolding for the creation of social cognition. Damasio, a neurobiologist, focused on the relationship between human emotions and human rationality, and he referred to these "senses" as background emotions. The discrete categories of affects and Damasio's term of background emotions both constitute a *separate* kind of experience than the dynamic forms of vitality. Content, sensations, and emotions can be disentangled from the dynamic forms of vitality. The dynamic forms of vitality occur, however, both in the presence of and in the absence of categorical affects (Stern, 2000).

Dynamic forms of vitality can be described in musical terms, such as fading away, decrescendo, swinging, accelerando, and so on. Forms of vitality are present and can be experienced in musical interplay but are not music per se (Johns, 2012; Papousêk & Papousêk, 1981). From a philosophical point of view, Langer (1942, p. 228) gave movement a fundamental role in feelings as she linked art (music) to the creation of forms as symbols of human feelings, suggesting that music sounds the way emotions feel to us. Pavlicevic (1990) examined the concept of dynamic forms as it relates to clinical improvisation in music therapy, but she did not apply Stern's (1985) notion of vitality affects. She suggested, however, that the dynamic forms, revealed through musical sounds, set the agenda of the improvisation.

Solo music making is also relevant to a music therapy process. Rose was an internationally renowned musician who had a passionately relationship to her instrument. "When I hold my instrument close, I am embracing my love," she said (Trondalen, 2013b, pp. 184-189). Rose was facing many physical health problems. She talked about being vitalized through the healing power of a music performance:

The fantastic sound of my instrument filled a gap in the orchestra, as it spread unto the room. ... I came to live again. I felt revitalized. I started to practice again and I feel I've started to live again. ... During the performance, I felt my quality of life was rising. ... Playing makes me good, gives me a kick. I am sure if I hadn't been able to play, I would have died. Playing again also contributed to healing my illness itself. ... Communicating with the audience is of vital importance. You *receive* signals from the audience that encourage you to *give*. ... The audience differs from place to place. I am looking for the one smiling face, and I maintain eye contact with that person. From her I receive a hope for—and expectation of—receiving something from me. It is a mutual process.

Rose felt vitalized and came alive during a special performance. Rather than focusing entirely upon the themes or phrases in the music or the musical actions as such, Rose found that the most important thing was the communication she felt with the audience. Such a process-based understanding of the mutual exchange between a musician and the audience privileges the communication above all else, and the stakes are high; "It's a mutual process ... music means life," she said (Trondalen, 2013b, p. 190).

Peter, a single 26-year-old man struggling with negative thoughts, hoped that GIM sessions would support him in his daily life, as he felt that he was not performing what was expected from him in his job. Peter received five individual GIM sessions over three months. At the last session, Peter listened to the music program *Mostly Bach*, with a total length of 45 minutes and 3 seconds (Bonny, 1977, as cited in Grocke, 2002a). The following transcript links to his listening experience during #3, Bach's "Little Fugue in G minor" (3 minutes 50 seconds). The fugue was performed with five saxophones.

I want to dance with angels—[*Do so, if you want to*]—we are flying and making a circle—[*Where are you?*]—I am a part of the circle—holding hands—we are moving up and down—no force of gravity—the earth and everything is

turning around—a very special feeling—everybody is
carrying a light—no words—pure spiritual joy—I feel
indeed protected—a strong power of light is protecting us.

The musical journey offered movement through the music as an
agent of force, driven forward by the client and his images in time and
space. The intensity and power of spiritual joy were evident,
according to Peter's reflections in the verbal conversation afterwards.

Qualities of music and movement are essential features of the
affective dialogue, and they connect to the human being's affective
state of mind—vitality. These forms of vitality are experienced
without cognitive processing. Music and movement do not relate to
cognitive processes per se, but to implicit relating experiences of how
to proceed together. Spontaneous musical expressions embed these
qualities. Dynamic forms of vitality, these inner experiences of being
alive, are always available, and they can easily be pursued and
explored through music making and music listening.

Chapter 6

Synchronization And Affect Attunement

Relational synchronization and regulation are evident in the development of early interaction and communication. The music therapy process links to mutual attunement on affects as well, as both dyadic synchronization and mutual regulation influence the relationship between a client and a music therapist.

Eye contact, smiling, mimicked expressions, gestures, and sounds are all elements in a rhythmic coordination and synchronization process within a relating experience. A mutual influence and sharing of non-verbal elements in an immediate and smooth form is the very first interaction between an individual and a caregiver. This face-to-face contact, including singing and speaking vowels, often called "motherese," establishes the basis for non-verbal communication and precedes later patterns of dialogical verbalization. Bateson (1975) called this early face-to-face exchange a "protoconversation." It is a primary format of an intersubjectivity (Trevarthen, 1980).

The typical pattern in this dialogical interaction is that the individual moves in and out of the interplay while the caretaker continuously looks at the child. The normal way of regulating includes interplay connected to interactive errors and repairs (Tronick, 1989). Through a regulation process, the individual learns that interactive stress is contemporary. Development is at risk if intense and negative affects are not regulated, such as due to neglect or abuse. Even the organic brain may be affected (Hansen, 2010; Siegel, 1999).

Research on mother-infant vocal interactions show an inborn musicality, independent of verbal communication. Thoroughly empirical analyses of such "dances of well-being" elucidate a shared sense of time and the shaping of jointly created pitch contours, which describe phrases and narrative cycles of feelings within an intersubjectivity matrix (Trevarthen & Malloch, 2000). Through rhythmic and vocal utterances, the individual exhibits the ability to partake, coordinate, and synchronize her or his expression in a mutually influencing dialogue. Such a pattern of interaction is a mutual, bidirectional way of regulating communication, evident to all human beings (Stern, 1995).

Furthermore, Stern's perspective on shift in intensity (level of activation) in mother-infant dyads is supported by research on vocal rhythms between mothers and adult strangers (Beebe et al., 2005). Accordingly, interactions consisting of musical elements embedded in form, intensity, and timing are evident to both infants and adults. From a therapeutic point of view, there may be a need for verbal processing to contextualize, develop, and interpret a musical interaction. However, this reworking is not necessary with regard to the origin of the interaction's immediate power (Trevarthen, 1999).

In a music therapy setting, the therapist is trying to modulate the client's level of stress and anxiety through mutually synchronized and attuned musical expressions. The music therapist is constantly aware of the client's utterances, whereas the client more often moves in and out of the interaction. Feelings and affects seem to be "contagious," for good and for bad. Allowing oneself to be affected by another person may be life-embracing or life-threatening, from an existential point of view. In music therapy, and in therapy in general, regulating the intensity of affects in an interpersonal relationship is a key challenge. Such a regulation is important to everybody but is of vital importance to a person struggling with illnesses and constraints. A relational perspective on music therapy with its focus on exchange through musical elements may provide a relating system supporting the regulation of overwhelming stress or intense affects within a safe musical frame.

Affect attunement is a term to elucidate the sharing of inner feelings states (Stern, 1985). In such a sharing, there is a matching going on, a crossmodal way of relating. This matching is not a direct imitation (Meltzoff & Gopnik, 1993), which is one possible way of dealing with observable behavior. Instead, the matching is connected to a crossmodal way of relating; i.e., the matching occurs in another modality than the original one. Accordingly, it is not the theme of the interaction (for example, song writing) or the musical code (e.g., the key) that stands out as most important, but the quality of the communication. What is at stake is *how* the interaction moves along (Stern, 2010).

Already in the second half of the first year, the individual perceives that inner senses can be shared through an empathic, regulated process. In such a sharing, a form of matching occurs. This matching is opposed to imitation, which relates to observable and overt behavior. Instead, it connects to an amodal way of relating; that is, the matching occurs in a different modality from the original one. This means that the person experiences both the form and the degree of a shared inner universe:

> What is being matched is not the other person's behavior per se but rather, it seems, some aspects of an internal feeling state. ... The match appears to occur between the expressions of inner state. ... We appear to be dealing with behavior as expressionism rather than as sign or symbol. (Stern, 1984, p. 5).

The process of attunement is an implicit (non-verbal) one based on micro-shifts with the essential elements of timing, intensity and form. Affect attunement emerges when the individual matches the person's movements and mental states in such a way that she or he experiences that these inner feeling states can be shared.

Such a non-verbal emotional experience may be recast as a *form of feeling*, which may function as a referent for an inner experience of matching and may finally facilitate symbolization (Stern, 1985). To Stern, affect attunement provides a bridge from the pre-symbolic to the symbolic mind. This theory "makes an important contribution to our understanding of the origins of symbolic forms of representation of feeling" (Beebe et al., 2005, p. 67). A lack of experience with affect attunement may lead to the assumption that one cannot be understood by others, which may lead to loneliness. Consequently, affect attunement is of major importance to mother-infant interactions, therapist-client relationships, and other kinds of relationships—indeed, to life in general.

Affect attunement may be observed at a practical level through dynamic and procedural qualities such as sound, gesture, and movement. There are, as previously clarified, three general features of a behavior that can be matched without necessarily being imitated: form, intensity, and timing. These characteristics, again, have some underlying matching criteria. These are (a) absolute intensity (for example, dynamics or rhythm), (b) intensity contour (e.g., melodic shape), (c) temporal beat (tempo changes in time), (d) rhythm (pattern of pulsation), (e) duration (time span), and (f) shape (features in time and space) (Stern, 1985, p. 146). Some of these dynamic and procedural qualities have similarities to music therapy techniques (see the 64 techniques listed by Bruscia, 1987).

Here is an illustration from expressive music therapy. Mothers and children gathered for group music therapy within the frame of a Child Welfare program. Three mothers (age 20 to 30) and three children (between 2 and 4 years) attended the group regularly for 10 sessions of 35 to 60 minutes. In the fifth session, the opening song was "Er Henrik kommet?" (Is Henrik Here?), composed by Sören Mühlhausen (n.d.). The lyrics was adapted and translated to the present setting. The song was in 4/4 time and the key of D major. The opening sequence elucidated the phenomenon of musical intersubjectivity, including crossmodal sharing. Guri, a 4 year old girl, interacted with me as follows (Trolldalen, 1997b; Trondalen, In press):

> Guri pointed at her head, saying "Me too." I was singing back to another girl, "Hello." During this answer, Guri was looking at me, singing "and me and me and me" while playing six tones intensely on the piano. I was making a big arm gesture, bowing toward her. I answered, laughing: "No, do you really think so?" She answered, "Yees" (I immediately confirmed with "yes"), while stretching her legs out sideways. "Is Guri here?" "*Yeah*". Loud chords at the piano: "*Yes, you are here.*" She slipped from her mother's lap and down on the floor. Short break. "We're sitting here singing, is Guri here?" "Yes, I'm rolling", she answered from the floor. I sang back while the rhythm in the song matched her rolling. "Yes, you're rolling around, and we're singing hello to you." Pause. The girl stayed on

the floor. I shifted the direction of my glance and changed
the rhythm in the music. Laughter from the group. The girl
crawled back to her mother's lap, and I asked the group,
"What are we going to do?" The next activity began.

What really stood out for me as the music therapist in this
sequence was the child's initiative to create a relation with the music
therapist through her look-at-me appeals ("and me and me," the
intensity in her voice, physical movements, eye contact and attention).
The girl knew the song activity very well and understood perfectly
well that her turn would come. This turn taking was clear due to the
structure in the previous session, in the external structure in this
session, through verbal communication and body language, and in the
musical frame with clear questions and answers. Even though I was
attuned to another two-year-old girl while singing "hello" to her, I was
indeed aware of the four-year-old girl striving to get my attention.
When I then gave Guri my full attention, I did so physically by eye
contact and a big arm movement intentionally directed toward her,
and verbally via humor at a meta-level ("No, do you really think so?").
She answered crossmodally with a smile, stretching her legs sideways.
This response was an attuned match in the music-making process,
with mutually observable attention in movement and rhythm.

Through rhythmic and vocal utterances, the child shows her
ability to partake, coordinate, and synchronize her expression in the
mutually influencing dialogue. Guri slid down to the floor and I
recognized this behavior (an intense experience, a feature in time and
space), and we maintained joint attention through the rhythm
(temporal beat) and melody. Guri answered my question and
confirmed that she was here (rhythmic and vocal utterances, "*Yeah*")
and expanded with "I'm rolling" as she started to roll. We continued
to coordinate and synchronize our expressions in a mutually
influencing dialogue when I put her answer ("yes, you're rolling") into
our common code-song. Mutual communication was maintained by
framing and exploring sound, gesture, and movement through music.
The musical activity allowed for exploration of how it was to be with
another person, in spite of different styles of interaction and age.

Following is an example of receptive music therapy from the same session. It lasted for 2 minutes and 19 seconds (Trolldalen, 1997a):

> The mothers and children were relaxing on the floor. The children had been stroking their mothers' cheeks while the music therapist played the piano and sang, "Stroking the cheek, stroking on mummy's cheek now." The intensity in the music was decreasing as one of the children looked at her mother with particular interest. The mother opened her eyes and smiled at her child, who immediately leaned toward her mother as the mother moved her body toward her girl. The mother simultaneously stretched her hand toward the child's cheek to pat it softly. Both smiled at each other while softly humming together, "Stroking the cheek, stroking it now."

The child and mother obviously shared a moment of joint attention and affect attunement, observed at the practical level through dynamic and procedural qualities such as gesture, movement, and the sound of their joint humming. The behavior of mutual attunement was noticeable through form, intensity and timing, which are in fact something different from imitation. From a therapeutic point of view, the girl was active and the mother received. At the end, they mutually adjusted toward each other while clearly sharing an attuned musical event. In my notes, I wrote that I was struck by the musical interaction's immediate power (Trondalen, In press). There seemed to be no need for verbal processing to contextualize, develop, or interpret the musical event.

In human interaction in general and in a musical dialogue, some kind of *selective attunement* will always be present in such a sharing of inner feeling states (Stern, 1985). Not all initiatives or inner feeling states are attuned. This creates some possibilities and some challenges. If the music therapist over- or under-attunes or does not attune at all, for example, toward a client's grief, this may lead to the feeling of not being existentially recognized, but isolated.

At other times, the music therapist may miss the opportunity to attune toward these inner feelings states due to lack of awareness, or may *mis-attune* in such a way that the possibility of a shared experience is lost. This may happen in daily conversation, in a music improvisation, or in a GIM session. The following example is drawn from a conversation between the client and the music therapist about a music improvisation. The client had been using "only" (in my interpretation) five notes (a pentatonic scale) while playing on a xylophone.

Cl: I think this music is grooving.
Th: *Yeah, don't you think?*
Cl: Yes, I reckon.
Th: *How was it to have such a limiting instrument?*
Cl: I don't think it was limiting.
Th: *No?*
Cl: I think it was more than enough. To me it was not limiting. I don't think xylophone is an especially beautiful instrument, but I like to play it. It gives a funny resonance.
Th: *Oh? Great. That's great!*
Cl: Yeah.

Happily, the client corrected the music therapist, as he stayed close to his own lived experience. Verbally, he rejected the idea that xylophone was a limiting instrument. The music therapist had been concerned that she was playing on the fancy, big grand piano and that the client would have felt limited on the xylophone. This assumption turned out to be incorrect (Trondalen, 2004a). Due to the client's correction of the music therapist's assumption, the music therapist could repair the verbal dialogue, which eventually led to recognition and the continuation of fruitful interaction.

Another example of mis-attunement could occur when a client plays some simple tones on a metallophone and the music therapist (with good intentions) picks up the same tones and transfers them to brilliant and embellishing music on the grand piano. This action may be perceived as *stealing the client's experience*. The music therapist does link to the client, but the client may be deprived of the experience of perceiving herself or himself as a person who can play and improvise. Accordingly, both miss out on enjoying a shared experience. The client does not experience being able to manage herself or himself and performing agency; instead, playing would become connected to low self-esteem and lack of control.

The importance of attunement is featured in Stern's (2000) concept of "the unity of senses." He highlighted there an integration of amodal (crossmodal) qualities of experiences like form, intensity, and time and connected unity of senses to how we perceive the world around us. Such a unified perception influences both the musical and relational interplay in therapy.

Chapter 7

Affect Integration And Mentalization

Toward the end of the second year, the individual develops a mental understanding of feelings and wishes, in addition to the ability to symbolize and use words. These two advances influence and expand the individual's affective communication, which takes on a new form. The person can now recognize the other person's subjective feelings and intentions (Bråten, 1998; Hansen, 2010). In doing so, the individual grasps that the feelings belong to another person, and not to herself or himself. This is evident whether or not the person responds to those perceived feelings. Such a development means an abstraction from immediate and concrete experience. New feelings and symbolic meaning emerge, and these novelties are especially explored through play.

By age three to four years, the individual is transforming experiences into self-biographic narratives. Cognitive, emotional, and relational aspects are knit together and merged into meaningful stories. The person understands that inner and outer realities affect each other, without being identical realities (Hansen, 2012; Stern, 2000). Mental representations of the world are used to construct reality. We share not the world itself but representations of it, while understanding ourselves and others as active contributors and co-creative individuals. This is "mentalization" or reflective function, "the idea of a relationship between attachment processes and the development of the capacity to envision mental states in self and others" (Fonagy, Gergely, Jurist, & Target, 2002, p. 23).

According to Bowlby (1988), attachment is crucial to survive. A person explores the world best from a secure base. Attachment theory, like most theories, has been revised and further developed over time through empirical studies and theoretical development. The present stance is that intersubjectivity should be considered as crucial for attachment (Brantzæg, Smith, & Torsteinson, 2011). Theories on mentalization or reflective function are rooted in evolutionary biology, neurobiology, attachment, and theory of mind (Fonagy & Target, 1997, 1998; Siegel, 1999). This tradition emphasizes that a secure base is not only crucial for surviving, but also a basis for the development of "reading oneself and others," or mentalization. Insecure attachment contributes to an interactional and relational vulnerability (Fonagy et al., 2002).

Mentalization is a key competence to promote regulation of feelings (Skårderud & Sommerfeld, 2008), and it refers to the developed ability to "read" one's own and other people's minds and the motivation for actions. For example, high inner arousal with reduced ability to regulate oneself may lead to a break down in mentalization, which is often due to earlier traumatic events experienced without the help of a safe adult to regulate and stabilize them. A mentalization-based approach to therapy is concerned for stabilizing the sense of self while supporting the client in optimally regulating arousal in the here-and-now. Mentalization is a developmentally and relationally important capacity for everybody. The mentalization process validates the experience of what we are doing and feeling as real, which contributes to the experience of being.

In everyday language, mentalization concerns recognizing and seeing oneself from an outside perspective and the other from an inside perspective, while interpreting implicit and explicit signals and utterances as meaningful expressions of inner life. Through one's own attentive imagination, the goal is to try to see the situation from the other's perspective, while maintaining one's own base (Fonagy et al., 2002; Fonagy & Bateman, 2006). Mentalization is a spontaneous and implicit (unconscious) process emerging from the encounter with one's own and the other's actions and feelings. The term also encompasses explicit language, symbols, and artefacts such as art and music. Mentalization is about identifying, interpreting, and understanding the other person *and* oneself as subjects on the basis of intentional mental states, including thoughts, intentions, and feelings in addition to desires, needs, beliefs, and reasons (Blom & Wrangsjö, 2013). The core of this function is to merge cognitive, emotional, and reflective perspectives into a meaningful unit while grasping and representing such a double reality through an endeavor to explore and recognize the relationship.

Social competence and communication are created slowly and emerge from experiences of successful mentalization (Brantzæg, Smith, & Torsteinson, 2011). At their foundation is an attentiveness toward the other's non-verbal signals such as mimicry, tone of voice, gestures, etc. Interestingly, a child with visual impairment develops mentalization as well, even though she or he might not mirror the other. Through neurotransmitter activity, the adult becomes attuned to the individual's mental state, and reacts in accordance with the individual's intentions (Bauer, 2007; Blom & Wrangsjö, 2013). The person experiences recognition of her or his inner states and mentalization develops.

What about mentalization and intersubjectivity? Mentalization is a process in which the person tries to create meaning based on mental states in oneself and the other, encountering the other's expressions and actions. The mentalization process generates focus and direction and functions as a resonator of the expressed affects. In this way, the mentalization, both explicit and implicit, is a driving force and an organizer of the flow of mental states between self and others within the intersubjective field (Blom & Wrangsjö, 2013, pp. 86–87). The capacity to mentalize is developed from an intersubjective relationship where affect attunement is a central trait in this process of creating meaning and understanding on the basis of implicit and explicit senses of self. Meaning and understanding link to the experience of sharing inner states, including what might be shared and what cannot be shared (Trondalen & Skårderud, 2007). The creation of shared meaning is based on exactly these experiences, aiming at "you know that I know that you know" and "I feel that you feel that I feel," i.e., intersubjectivity.

Mentalization and the link to expressive and receptive music therapy have been elucidated in recent texts (Hannibal, 2014a, 2014b; Metzner, 2016; Strehlow, 2009, 2013). Recent discoveries suggest that mentalization-based therapy may represent a turning from psychoanalytic therapy focusing on interpretation of embedded concepts (e.g., transference), toward an increased focus on the here-and-now, that is, implicit relational learning and context (Hannibal, 2013; Hannibal et al., 2013). In expressive music therapy, for example,

61

a client's resistance to playing is no longer interpreted as resistance (*Widerstand*) in psychoanalytical terms. Instead, it is a reaction to the music making's potential arousal of insecure attachment patterns. Frohne-Hagemann (2015) emphasized the need to consider sociological and psychological dimensions of mentalization, that is, how "mentalized information is dependent on situations, cultural traditions, norms, and attitudes" (p. 170).

Music is, however, a multilayered phenomenon. The attention is drawn to music as a whole or to certain layers at a micro level (Trondalen & Wosch, In press). The mentalization process seems to be included in many of the different layers of experience. In expressive music therapy, the mentalization process emerges during interplay through the encounter of intentional mental states—thoughts, intentions, feelings, desires, needs, beliefs and reasons, whether audible or visible in the music making. It may be verbally investigated after the joint music creation.

In receptive music therapy, such as mentalization-based GIM, the mentalization process also emerges during the music journey through the meeting of mental states:

> The guiding of a mentalization-based GIM session seems to support a synchronizing activation of the client's left and right brain hemisphere in coordination with the prefrontal cortex. ... The mentalization process takes place in all these layers. Feeling is necessary to find metaphors, and visual imagery needs the perception of the underlying emotional qualities in order to coordinate the musical experiences in the right and left hemisphere. (Frohne-Hagemann, 2015, p. 171)

The encounter in GIM includes the sharing of inner mental states. These mental states are mediated through images, which are continually stimulated and contextualized by the music, and also by the music therapist's comments. These mental states are explored through drawings ("mandalas") and verbal communication afterwards. The aim is to process dynamic forms of vitality and categorical affects from the right brain-hemisphere verbally in the left brain-hemisphere. I would add, though, that contemporary neuroscience and brain research focus on the brain's plasticity while also stressing the importance of cooperation between the two parts of the brain, not least when it comes to processing music (Levitin, 2007; Sachs, 2006, 2007). The interpretation through words and symbols emerges on the basis of the shared music experience.

The following example comes from expressive music therapy. Charles, a resourceful 28-year-old man, attended music therapy for half a year while studying at the university. Charles found it extremely difficult to be in emotional contact with his body; the body became an object to him ("embodiment"; Duesund & Skårderud, 2003) as opposed to his having a living and vital body, that is, a subjective connectedness to himself. He very much wanted to be more "lively and vigorous." In Charles's second session, an improvisation lasting 2 minutes 50 seconds took place. Prior to the musical improvisation, the music therapist had suggested lining up two percussion instruments on a table, a metallophone, and a xylophone. The music therapist played the piano; the key was C pentatonic. The client initiated a rhythmic pattern, and the music therapist followed and suggested melodic embroideries. Suddenly Charles stopped and the following conversation took place, with Charles taking the lead role:

Cl: This *is* Charles. You know, now I heard something strange.
Th: *Okay? Tell me more.*
Cl: Listen to this. When I play the metallophone, it is alive. Listen to this [i.e., the xylophone]; this is only "knock, knock" [playing short, dry beats with the mallet]. This is Charles. The other one [i.e., the metallophone] is more like—it is the way I would like to be. I want to be more lively and vigorous, but everything becomes like this [he plays broken-up notes, with an unstable beat, in the high tremble with his mallets on the xylophone]. Listen, it is like "listen to me." It is strange; I suddenly heard it while playing. ... [with a spontaneous smile] It's quite fun, actually.

Charles suddenly realized he was acting out ("projecting") himself through his playing: "This *is* Charles." He seized himself, recognizing that he resonated with the xylophone. He then realized that he was longing for something different, recognizable to him through the metallophone. Charles became aware of his feelings. The symbolic use of the instruments seemed to provide a link between his inner and outer realities. During the music therapy experience itself, Charles acquired an experience of self-agency. The therapist's role was to support this experience. In this situation, the music therapist's presence was an enabling condition for mentalization. Mentalization is a way of developing the self, a development process (Fonagy et al., 2002). The mentalization process seemed to validate Charles's living and thinking body, which was able to perceive and to grasp at the same time (Merleau-Ponty, 1962).

Receptive music therapy approaches, especially GIM in individual or group settings, often seem to speed up the process from regulation to mentalization. A 25-year-old musician, Anders, struggled to connect with and surrender to the music. He said that he often experienced the notes as standing between him and his instrument. This experience inhibited his rehearsals and influenced his performance on stage as well. In the third of five sessions, he had this experience (Trondalen, 2016a):

> I'm standing in the middle of the music—it is huge—
> [*Dwell within the experience as long as you want to*]—I'm
> in the middle of a twister—[*Is there anything you are
> aware of?*]—a few seconds ago it was a whirlpool—now
> a pleasant breeze—I'm now in the middle of a meadow.

In this twister experience, Anders managed to let go and surrender (Blom, 2014) in a secure music therapy setting. Surrender requires trusting the relationship in a way that allows the therapist to be an enabling condition for mentalization. In the illustration, music supported intersubjectivity in a genuine way. After the music journey, Andres represented his twister experience in a drawing, visualizing the twister itself. Thereafter, the living and embodied experience as a whole was explored in a verbal conversation. We talked about his drawing, "The Twister." To support symbolization and enhance mentalization, the verbal conversation covered how the actual image related to him as a performing musician as well (Fonagy et al., 2002). It turned out that Anders was able to experience himself as intentional in relation to the music therapist—that is, to perform self-agency (the experience of being separate and still in relation) within a relationship, or to have an experience of intersubjectivity.

Anders later told me that he was able to recall his twister experience on stage while performing and that he had received excellent reviewers. I suggest that the GIM experience provided building blocks for the musician's inner mental representations, bridging the gap between affects and their representations, that is, supporting mentalization. Linking experiences through music with verbalizing and making connections to real-life events support a closer connection between the physical or mental and existential dimensions of life. I propose that a musical relating experience, followed by verbal processing, can provide a link between body and mind and subsequently support a more coherent sense of self. Hence, a musical narrative based on a real experience may contribute to semantic meaning, which supports symbolic emergence (Trondalen, 2016a). At a meta-theoretical level, this connection between personal, transpersonal, and social spaces (Ruud, 1997/2013) both arises from and supports a personal and professional identity as an individual. Consequently, in this case it related the musician's self-understanding to a narrative structure.

Chapter 8

Self, Intersubjectivity, And Recognition

The notion of *self* is understood and interpreted in many different ways, based on a variety of theoretical orientations and approaches (Karterud & Monsen, 1997; Thorsteinsson, 2000). Terms such as *subject, subjectivity, identity*, and *person* are linked to the term *self*. In therapy, most often the development of self is connected to an individual, inner process. Bateson (1973), however, underscored the connection between individual conditions and contexts.

The present text addresses a relational self-formation process (musical-relational interaction), next to a belief in the subjective aspect within the recognition process. On one hand, I would suggest that the dialogical interaction is crucial as an evolving principle. On the other hand, I recognize the philosophical aspect: "One can never know any other person by referring to oneself" (Ihlen & Ihlen, 2003). Put another way, the self is formed and relies on the dialogue with others to develop itself, but the self is, from a philosophical viewpoint, fundamentally unknowable to the other. Accordingly, descriptions will always be ambiguous and multilayered in understanding of the self.

Theoretically, Stern (2000) has influenced my understanding of development, change, and growth. He linked self-development directly to the individual's subjective experience of the relationships in which that individual partakes and which she or he co-creates. This implies that the relational interaction is seen as a self-organizing fundamental perspective, while the person participates in the relationship on the basis of her or his inborn personality:

> We instinctively process our experience in such a way that they appear to belong to some kind of unique subjective organization that we commonly call the sense of self. ...

Accordingly it must be asked, what kind of sense of self might exist in a preverbal infant? By "sense" I mean simple (non-self-reflexive) awareness. We are speaking at the level of direct experience, not concept. (Stern, 2000, pp. 6–7).

The self also includes non-verbal and implicit conditions. Stern suggested that its development will be due to different layers of "senses of self": that is, to exist in the world as somebody, while also constructing the world on basis of relational experiences with others. This description reflects Stern's connections to phenomenology, as he treated self as a basic category to elucidate how it is to be a human being in the world. In sum, the self is always related to *all* our experiences, including body, mind, and soul.

Human beings have different positions in the world, but they are inextricably linked to one another through the wholeness that they create (Thorsteinsson, 2000). The self is tied to *time* and *event*, as an integrated unity. On this basis, it is interesting to look at the constitution and function of language. First, language is an agent of taking care of earlier lived experiences, experienced in different modes from the verbal one. Second, language may support the creation of and eventually transform earlier experiences through the narrated history. Hence, the story is narrated on the basis of relating bodily-musical experiences.

The self contains a subjectively lived experience (existing), which is modulated and regulated in the actual context (created). In this way, the context includes a variety of components at different levels, such as interpersonal relational contexts in a broad sense. This again, is placed against the background of societal and cultural conditions at a structural level. Our identity, then, or our sense of social and cultural belonging, always arises from a combination of interior (genetic) and exterior (contextual) conditions. Accordingly, a human being's self and identity represent an intra and interdisciplinary construct, connected to the self-in-context and related to both an individual and a relational perspective (Engedal, 1989; Stern, 2000).

From a philosophical point of view, Honneth (1995) introduced a three-part model of the struggling for recognition synthesizing a variety of perspectives. The first phase in his model was linked to the primary relations, to the demand for love (emotional commitment). The second was the claim for rights, (cognitive respect, self-respect). The last, phase three, was the call for solidarity (social recognition). These three forms are mutually influencing each other (Trondalen, In press).

The present chapter links primarily to the first phase in Honneth's model, while focusing *intersubjectivity* and *recognition* as building blocks for development and growth (see, also, chapter 12, Power and Responsibility). This text highlights the intersubjective process with its inherent focus on both explicit and implicit knowledge concerning what to think and feel in a specific relational context, whether it be in music therapy or in a daily life setting. An intersubjective perspective holds affect attunement as a core element (Stern, Hofer, Haft, & Dore, 1985). The individual perceives herself or himself as separate from another, as a separate entity with her or his personal inner life (Schibby, 1991). An important point for the client will therefore be to recognize a "response" to her or his own inner life by investigating which feeling states are possible to share with others—and which are not. This process occurs partly through an amodal affective exchange at a practical level. From a theoretical point of view, intersubjectivity seizes the main core of recognition when two persons meet each other through mutuality, empathy, and sharing of joint attention.

Benjamin (1990, 2004) suggested that the intrapsychic and intersubjective aspects of self-development are complementary. She referred to Hegel as a source of inspiration, as recognition is included in his dialectic understanding of relations. In such a philosophical framework, recognition always means mutual recognition. The persons relate to one another as one subject to another. Recognition is about seizing the other's mental awareness and returning such an awareness as recognized by my mental awareness (Schibby, 2009). It concerns taking time to explore, wonder, and be surprised together with the client, as a way of being. In music therapy practice, recognition includes listening, understanding, confirmation, acceptance, and tolerance, both in words and in the musical interplay. These concepts are complementary and partly overlapping with each other. Mutual recognition is a core element of intersubjectivity:

> Intersubjective theory postulates that the others must be recognized as another subject in order for the self to fully experience her or his subjectivity in the other's presence. This means, first, that we have a need for recognition and second, that we have capacity to recognize others in return—mutual recognition. (Benjamin, 1990, p. 35)

Recognition means something different from and more than positive feedback and praise. When a music therapist praises a client, that implies some form of judgment (conscious or unconscious) of what the other person is doing. Such praise implies that the event or feeling is valued as "right" from the music therapist's point of view. This feedback does not mean that the client is becoming aware of her or his own experience or feeling. On the contrary, praise may function in such a way that the client's personal experience becomes unclear, because inherent in this kind of feedback is an element of gratitude to the music therapist giving the praise. Accordingly, the praise may lead to ongoing non-differentiation and dependence, rather than to a separated and independent relation to one's own experiences. This pattern is also evident in daily life encounters.

For an example from expressive music therapy, I will once again refer to the group of young mothers and children that I have cited earlier. This illustration (the activity lasted 2 minutes 19 seconds) emphasizes the nature of mother and child as a pair (Trolldalen, 1997a, p. 20):

> The mothers and children had been playing on the floor. One mother returned quickly to her chair. The rest of the group members were still lying on the floor when the music therapist asked, "What can we do next?" One of the children said, "Stand up." We stood up and the music therapist said, "Everybody can stand and hold each other's hand." Everybody was singing and dancing in a circle: "Yes, we are dancing together now, dancing together now." After

a short while (about 20 seconds), I changed the text to "dancing with mummy, dancing now" and moved to the piano. The circles dissolved and the mother-and-child dyads were moving toward each other. The mother at the chair moved toward her child upon hearing the lyrics. The mothers and children danced together as pairs. One of the children jumped up to her mother, who immediately raised him up and swung him around. Shortly after that, all the mothers began lifting and swinging their own children high in the air. I picked up on the activity while singing: "Swinging around, do it now, swinging around up high." Lots of laughter and fun.

The present activity initiated from one child suggesting that we should stand up. I recognized the idea, offered a familiar melody, and introduced the lyrics "dancing together now." Joining in a group again offered a renewed attentiveness (dancing together). I intentionally changed the lyrics to "dancing with mummy" to support the joining of dyads. The children and the mothers recognized the change and immediately moved intentionally towards each other. The resting mother got up and moved to meet her child, who was already coming toward her. All dyads joined the dancing. I recognized the initiatives of the pairs (swinging around up high) by giving them a musical form (bonding). To encourage upholding the constructive play between mother and child, I repeated the rhythm, melody, and text. From these musical actions, they had the opportunity to recognize each other and the joy of having their expectations fulfilled from the music therapist (e.g., swinging around up high). It was obvious that playing together through improvisation offered a certain safe frame to explore musical improvising through their living and perceiving bodies together. One might wonder if it is through music therapy as improvisation that *playing* shows its real "face" (Stensæth, 2014).

Ole, a man in his mid-fifties, was curious about GIM because this music therapy method offered the chance to listen to classical music, for which he had a strong affection. He attended five GIM sessions over a six-month period in an individual and private practice setting, hoping to improve his low self-confidence as a professional musician so that he could continue to enjoy his musicianship in a very demanding daily life. Based on our preliminary discussion, I chose the music program *Peak Experience (Modified)*[1]. While listening to Beethoven's Fifth Piano Concerto, Ole talked about letting go of worries. "In Terra Pax" by Vivaldi reminded him of his personal calling to convey the wonderful experience of music to everybody. During the Bach, he focused on peace on earth: "The music talks about entering into a greater freedom—greater life—ongoing growth." During Fauré's *Requiem* (In Paradisum), Ole said:

> Is this Fauré's Requiem?—[*It is*]—I am thinking of the word of Jesus: "Peace I leave with you, my peace I give unto you: not as the world giveth, give I unto you"— it's a promise that we already can acquire peace in the midst of all noise — the music is lifting us out of the daily life—a taste of paradise [*Take your time—dwell in the experience*].

Ole's drawing ("mandala") was colored in a square pattern, with circles at the top, drawn in yellow, red, blue, orange, and two black lines, that suggested a rainbow. In the Bible (Genesis 9:13 and 15), with which the client was familiar, the rainbow is the sign of a new beginning after the great flood. Ole titled the drawing, "The Wandering Hand."

In Paradisum is the seventh and last movement in Fauré's choral-orchestral setting of the "Mass for the Dead" in D minor. The text *In paradisum deducant te Angeli* ("May the angels lead you into paradise") also includes *Chorus angelorum te suscipiat, et ... æternam habeas requiem* ("May choirs of angels welcome you ... may you find eternal rest"). The music is composed for a four-part choir and has a sustained tranquility and peacefulness (Grocke, 2002a). "The music spoke so beautifully to me today," Ole said. It was a spiritual and

---

1. This program is *Peak Experience Modified,* and lasts for 31 min. 41 sec. (Bonny & Bruscia, 1996, in Bruscia, 2014b). The present *Music for the Imagination* (MFI) version has one change from Bonny's original program: Bach's Sixth Brandenburg Concerto has been substituted for his orchestrated Adagio in C (Grocke, 2002a).

confirming experience (Abrams, 2002), offering him a "taste of paradise" in the here-and-now. He felt recognized as the person he was. In such an existential experience of being, Ole said it was important to him to link to the music therapist outside the experience. I assume that he meant it was important to receive appreciative recognition from the therapist, such as "dwell in the experience," as opposed to more critical comments such as those from a previous teacher. The existential experience included recognition, which may be understood as an intersubjective experience. In addition, the lived experience seemed to support another track of connecting to non-verbal and unconscious past experiences (Lyons-Ruth, 1998), as these inner experiences of being alive in the musical journey also stayed with him outside the music therapy setting.

The genuine recognition and understanding of the other in music therapy may happen through a sensitive awareness in the musical dialogue and the verbal exploration. In music therapy practice, this may entail a sensitive and attuned exchange of musical elements, gestures, and actions, where musical codes and emotional availability enable appreciative recognition at an existential level. In the verbal exploration, one might say, for example, "I would like to hear more; would you like to say more?" or "I really enjoyed playing on the drum together with you today. I wonder how it was for you?" This kind of dialogue and appreciative recognition are based on a willingness to "let oneself go" in favour of the other. This accepting and awareness of the other from her or his own point of view is not as obvious in standard praise. The possibility of meaning-making seems to be present in both expressive and receptive music therapy (Trondalen, 2007a). On this basis, intersubjectivity and recognition are building blocks for development and growth while promoting new ways of relating. This implies that intersubjectivity has a relational dimension in itself.

Chapter 9

The Music Therapy Relationship

What is music, and what does music mean in a music therapy context? The answers vary in wording, theoretical, and philosophical approach and in level of reflexivity. Music is not a reflection of an idea (consider the Greeks' view of music; Sundberg, 1980). "Music is what people experience as music," Benestad (1976, p. 411) suggested. Such a view includes cultural factors, self-interest, and social belonging. A famous formulation from 1940, "Music is organized sound," originated with Edgar Varèse. He said, "I prefer to use the expression 'organised sound' and avoid the monstrous question: 'But what is music?' " (in Bengtsson, 1973/1977, p. 2). The definitions show obvious differences, here exemplified by one socio-cultural and one physically measurable approach to music. This simply intensifies the questions. One issue at stake is whether music has any essential, inherent meaning or if it is reducible to physical fluctuations measured in time (Bonde, 2009). Theoretical discourse about music considers it as a qualitative and aesthetic expression and asks whether music is a form of communication and/or a separate language, with the meaning of music lying in the meeting between the music and the listener. These seemingly simple questions highlight different ontological positions (Bengtsson, 1973/1977; Ruud, 2005).

Aigen (2014, p. 45) suggested, "Music represents an alternative experiential realm, a different type of phenomenal world for those who can exist in it." Garred's (2001) elaboration of the ontology of music in music therapy led Kenny (2002) to ask whether we should really be looking for an ontology, or if we are trying to discover what is unique about music therapy? Kenny recognized the need for theory building and development. However, she questioned whether music therapy really needs its very own definition of music. Initially, this means that music does not have the status of being *work* in a classical musicological tradition (Benestad, 1976). In music therapy, music connects to all human beings' ability and need to act and express themselves through music, whether in an expressive or a receptive mode. Music has an aesthetic and a communicative function.

Musical actions involve both communication and interaction (Ruud, 1990). Music as communication and interaction has greatly influenced new musicology and music therapy, though it has had less influence in music psychology, according to Bonde (2009). From this point of view, a musical performance in a music therapy setting also can be read as an open expression and/or symbol that offers added value and meaning, regardless of one's ontological position.

Stige (2003; see also Ansdell, 2014; Rolvsjord, 2010; Ruud, 1998) has recommended seeing music in a cultural and social context. He drew attention to the term *musicking* (Small, 1998), meaning any activity involving or related to a music performance, that is, music as action and interaction in social and cultural contexts (Stige, 2002). Musicking affords construction of meaning, which is appropriated by the participations within a variety of contexts (DeNora, 2000, 2013). How meaning is appropriated depends on the actual context. Stige's (2003) use of *musicking* in a social context embraces everyday uses of music for health purposes as well (see, also, Bonde, 2011).

My understanding is that Stige was suggesting a meta-understanding of the concept of music, one based on protomusicality, participatory musical performances ("musicking") in addition to "musics" (many ways of making and interpreting music in a cultural context). He thus recognized the interpersonal, biological, and cultural aspects of participatory musical performances. First, Stige referred to protomusicality (Bateson, 1975), in that an individual is born with a biological preference for human contact, which makes contextual communication and learning possible. Accordingly, a communicative musicality (Trevarthen & Malloch, 2000), or the dynamic, sympathetic state of a human person that allows coordinated companionship to arise, appears. Core elements are joint timing, joint formation of a melodic contour, texture and intensity, and a joint or shared narrative form. Such a protomusicality is about human capacity for creating artifacts through non-verbal expression. Second is "music-in-context," or participation in the actual musical performance within a social context. In this respect, musicking is an action. Participatory music activities become both an activity and a joint relationship. Third, "musics" is linked to many ways of making and understanding music ("diversity of cultural artefacts with a variety of affordances", Stige, 2003, p. 172), and in that sense, it is not reserved for a particular style or genre. The point is that the music performed in a music therapy setting stands for many types of musics; it is thus independent of concepts like "right" and "wrong" or of status as defined by a given value-laden theory or social system. In the middle of this triangle, the life story is located. This life history filters through and is influenced by protomusicality, musics, and musicking. In this context, Stige (2003, p. 172) interpreted a life story as "cultivated capacities and perceived affordance."

I recognize Stige's embrace of many layers of a musical life perspective, focusing on participation. When we explore these ideas in music therapy, however, it does seem that they are less investigated in relation to receptive approaches in music therapy (such as GIM), as opposed to expressive methods. Furthermore, I miss an emphasis on the participating musical *body*. In an improvisation, the client quite often moves rhythmically to the music and uses her or his body intentionally to express inner states or feelings through music. This is opposed to an instrumentalization of the body. The performance by the client's subjective body very often seems to promote vitality and the feeling of being alive (Trondalen & Skårderud, 2007). In listening sessions like GIM, clients report on a variety of experiences, including body experiences (Goldberg, 2002; Grocke, 1999). For example, they may feel the musical intervals in their arms while playing an instrument, freedom while stretching their arms as if standing on top of a mountain, or an altered state of bodily being such as an extraordinary huge ear or arm.

I suggest emphasizing the musical body as a perceiving, participating, and imaginative transforming body (for example, through transpersonal experience) both in music making and music listening. This connects to the *living body* (Merleau-Ponty, 1962), which is experiencing, sensing, acting, and seeking meaning through reflection and actions. Such a phenomenal body has an inborn capacity of double-sensing, i.e., the ability to grasp (psychically) and perceive (mentally) at the same time from an inside perspective.

A living body, though, does not materialize independent of mundane categories and contexts. Everything has a certain pattern and frame, a certain "order" (see Kant's aesthetic turn as elaborated by Nietzsche; Storheim, 1993). In music therapy practice, the client and therapist offer their being, doing, and symbolizing in a joint yet not identical field of musical exploration. Whatever the client and music therapist may carry with them into the relational music experience, their musical experiences will function only as a starting point, as the experiences always are interpreted in the present context. The aesthetic communication (expressive or receptive) in the relational music experience is the living and sensing participation itself.

The music in these relating experiences is both an agent in itself and a tool of dialoguing, encouraging an immediate mutuality, since the sharing of experiences is evident in the musical process. That is not to say that the music automatically induces specific feelings, bodily reactions, or existential experiences (referential or expressionistic; Bonde, 2009). On the contrary, the music offers a variety of emotions and interpretations, allowing the individual to explore what is most powerful or evident to her or him during the musical experience.

Sometimes nomenclature from music is used to describe phenomena related to these interpersonal qualities and relations. Knoblau (2000, p. 95) put forward the term "resonant minding," pointing out that musical elements in the verbal dialogue are valuable sources of information with regard to unconscious communication and the actions in the dyadic psychotherapeutic relationship. Stern (2010) used musical terms to elucidate dynamic forms of vitality embedded in all human interaction. These forms of vitality are continuously present and can be experienced in musical play but are not music per se (Eriksson, 2001; Johns, 2012; Rolvsjord, 1996). Johns (1993, p. 46; my translation) concluded:

> We find the same basic features of the preverbal interaction and the musical interaction. When the music therapist utilizes the knowledge of these basic features,

such as regulation and sensitive adaptation, she will contribute to increased interaction skills and interests, and thus to greater initiative, assertiveness, and development.

There are different terms to describe musical togetherness in a musical relationship, such as interplay, interaction, and communication (Trolldalen, 1997a). *Interplay* relates to the dynamic attunement process that characterizes companionship between two or more participants when they are "wandering together." It does not necessarily include an intentional action per se. It is the experience of togetherness or of "being on the same wave length" that is crucial in enabling mutual influence while two people are trying to establish, maintain, and develop an interpersonal relationship (Tønsberg & Hauge, 1996). I would suggest that musical interplay is the dynamic and vibrant adaptation process characterized by togetherness in the here-and-now in the musical relationship.

The concepts of interaction and communication are often used interchangeably. They vary somewhat in content, partly based on the particular theoretical model used. To clarify the term *communication* and lead it closer to music therapy practice, Ruud (1990) suggested using *interaction* in addition to *communication*. The aim is to highlight that communication in music therapy does not imply a transport model of communication. Instead, music therapy includes a complicated process of mutual influence in which the participants take part. Ruud stated, "The musical interaction is a concrete expression of an exchange of musical actions between a number of people" (1990, p. 23; my translation). The concept of musical interaction is intended to clarify the exchange of musical actions that usually occur in music therapy. However, not all actions are necessarily referential, nor do they hold symbolic meaning. The client and therapist actively engage in a joint musical creation, be it expressive or receptive music therapy. In short, *interaction* includes a concrete exchange of interpersonal and musical gestures and actions, which do not necessarily carry a specific message or hold symbolic meaning in themselves. The concept of *communication,* on the other hand, contains generalized actions with observable intentional content. An example may be the client who sits on an African drum. She looks at the therapist, who looks at her, saying "play on," and the client intentionally starts her drumming.

The concept of music (including musical togetherness) is indeed not a static or fixed term in music therapy. It varies due to theoretical choices, the individual's cultural music tradition, and the therapist's experience with various populations in music therapy practice. It also relates to philosophical and theoretical orientations, as well as to personal reflexivity. Finally, I want to enhance the significance of music as an art form. Music is multilayered (Trondalen, 2005a) and is experienced through very different strata such as an existential level (being), as an action (doing), and a transformation (symbolization) of reality within a musical experience.

Developmentally, the fetus experiences music during gestation (Theorell, 2009). Qualitative studies have shown that pregnant women experience contact with their unborn child during musical performances (de Labbé; 2010; Marstal, 2008), and children seem to remember songs being sung to them during pregnancy (Mulelid, 2004). The human being seems to have an inborn biological preference for music (Fagius & Lagercrantz, 2007). There is however, no specific center in the brain for music alone. Both hemispheres of the great brain, the cerebrum, have to cooperate through different functions (Fagius, 2001; Levitin, 2007).

Music therapy practices include music making and music listening in different variations and utilize the client's musical experience as the primary methodology. In music therapy, different aspects of life are investigated through four distinct types of musical experience: improvising, recreating (or performing), composing, and listening (Bruscia, 2014a). A sense of relating through music emerges during a musical experience in an individual inpatient setting at a psychiatric ward (Odell-Miller, 2007), as well as within a social context such as musicking at a café (Ansdell & DeNora, 2016). Music appears as a *direct* experience, which acquires meaning in the present relationship.

A musical experience in music therapy involves a universal human encounter where dynamic and procedural qualities such as sound, gestures, and movement promote, maintain, and develop the musical relationship. It includes audible expressions that unfold in time, dynamics, and form, while also containing visible gestures and sound expressions, given meaning in the musical context. The music in these experiences, I believe, has value in itself. However, the value and meaning of music are not simply limited to an inherent human aesthetic means of expression or a modality of experience. It is neither reduced simply to sound and to physics or to a social construct, as such reductions would remove the musical (intra- and interpersonal) qualities that constitute a musical experience. Nor is the music understood as a reflection of an idea. It appears as a direct, lived experience.

A musical experience may go beyond the individual's limited, controlled self as well. It may touch the human being's deepest value as a creation, supporting unity and integrational experiences in a person's life. A relating experience through music is an invitation, a welcome to surrender and to dwell in a musical presence. When such an existential musical experience occurs, it is received as a gift (Trondalen, 2012).

The *therapeutic relationship* has many interpretations. With reference to a psychodynamic therapy tradition, "The power of change lies in the relationship that arises, and in the self-reflection that this relation makes possible. There is always talk of an attachment process" (Haugsgjerd, Jensen, & Karlsson, 1998, p. 172). In line with this, Killingmo (1999) highlighted the importance of an "opening conversation." He chooses deliberately the word *opening* as opposed to *open*, to emphasize that the conversation does not endeavor to open up completely. The important thing is to create a respectable dynamic between opening and closing forces in the conversation. Rogers (1951/1965), from his phenomenological-existential position, focused on universal phenomena such as unconditional love and empathic understanding, in addition to communicating these qualities to clients.

Research has focused on necessary and sufficient factors in psychotherapy, which are included in the broader term *therapeutic alliance* (Axelsen & Hartmann, 1999; Wormnes, 2013). Within a humanistic-existential tradition, Yalom (2001) advocated an "authentic attitude" within a direct relationship, suggesting that the patient and therapist should be "fellow travellers, a term that abolishes distinctions between 'them' (the afflicted) and 'us' (the healers). ... We are all in this together and there is no therapist and no person immune to the inherent tragedies of existence" (p. 8). Such an existential attitude reflects a foundation for psychotherapy that abolishes the other as an objectified "thing." The client and therapist are subjects to each other, at both a philosophical and a practical level. This mirrors a therapeutic attitude and thereby is not a denial of the therapeutic responsibility in the relationship itself.

In a therapeutic relationship, one person is termed the client and the other is the therapist (Bruscia, 2014a). I think that to reject such a thought at the practical level does not take into account the deep responsibility involved in being a therapist. Neither the client nor the therapist can walk in and out of a relationship, as the relationship itself frames and possibly expands the interactions between them. There is not an objectified relationship, a thing, between client and therapist. The fluency of musical interaction provides a flexible framework in which positions change during the interaction. Therapist and client change roles as living subjects and objects to each other (Garred, 2006). Sensing the interplay, being together in the music-making and music listening relationship— performing intersubjectivity—may give meaning to life itself.

An intersubjective relationship is multifaceted, from a clinical, theoretical, and philosophical standpoint. An interesting question presents itself: how mutual can a therapeutic relationship really be? One more perspective is the authority that the therapist represents in the relationship by virtue of her title and academic qualifications. I believe that such an authority has to be made conscious and "tamed." The therapist should never act, even unconsciously, as a "doorkeeper of the mind" (Kolnes, 1998). A doorkeeper's role may include an external and eventually internal authority that gradually steals the client's freedom and enforces a life based on the therapist's norms and values rather than the client's.

The *music therapy relationship* is established through music and is interactive in nature. Relationship in music therapy includes intramusical, intermusical, intrapersonal, and interpersonal aspects. In addition, one must consider each human being's personal relationship to music and ecological relationships, such as contextual aspects:

> The professional services of a music therapist are defined
> and delimited by those health concerns of the client *that*
> *can be addressed through music.* Although this may seem
> obvious and redundant to say, the primary job of a music
> therapist is to provide clients with music experiences
> aimed at promoting health. (Bruscia, 2014, p. 70)

Expressive and receptive music therapy allow for experiences at different levels through a present aesthetic participation within a multilayered frame of interpretation (Trondalen, 2005a). Such a musical relationship, based on empowerment and attunement, supports affirmative, corrective, emotional, and relational experiences through music, and it defines music therapy as a specific health promoting practice (Trondalen & Bonde, 2012).

Music therapists work in different ways, emerging from their clinical orientation, and have different areas and levels of practice (Bruscia, 1998). The music therapy relationship may be seen as a means of expression and symbolic action, focusing on the unconscious through music and verbal exploration. A music therapy relationship in line with a psychoanalytic tradition may focus on transference and projective identification in the musical and interpersonal relationship (Alvin, 1966/1975; Eschen, 2002; Lecourt, 1991; Priestley, 1975/1985). Psychoanalytically oriented music therapy embeds music making and verbal processing (Austin, 1999; Metzner, 2016; Mössler, 2010). When one works with people who have reduced language capacity, music enables self-expression and communication as well, even where learning disabilities or physical limitations may be substantial (Elefant, 2002; Holck, 2004; Ridder, 2003). Music is indeed a relational power in itself (Bonny, 1976, 2002; Lee, 1996; Nordoff & Robbins, 1977). The music therapy relationship may also explicitly be linked to human rights (Krüger, 2012; Stige, 2002), increased possibilities of action (Næss & Ruud, 2007; Ruud, 1990), and recovery (Henser, McFerran, Killacky, & McGorry, 2015; Procter, 2002; Solli & Rolvsjord, 2015).

Additionally, as far as clinical orientation is concerned, my experience is that it is not typical of music therapy practice to categorize an entire session or an entire method as *either* music as therapy *or* music in therapy. During joint music making and music listening procedures, music may act in both ways, changing from moment to moment.

Garred (2006) emphasized the nature of the therapeutic relationship as an immediate interpersonal presence, an attitudinal mode with which music is met. With reference to Buber (1970), Garred (2006, p. 71-72) pointed to the creative encounter:

> It is not like an "objective", purely technical course of action in which the outcome is dependably known and counted on beforehand, as in some regular procedures for certain predefined tasks dealt with on a regular basis in daily life. What comes out of the creative act is never completely known beforehand. There is a risk involved, an uncertainty. Making music can never be completely predetermined, or else it was simply not creative, not something new that was brought forth.

Garred (1996) called attention to the relational qualities that contribute to the interaction and to the development of a therapeutic relationship, but without omitting or reducing the role of music. This resonates with my own understanding of a relationship in music therapy. It all starts as a direct and immediate interpersonal relationship that develops in the present, expands, and changes during the musical interplay.

Furthermore, within the encounter itself, the "non-regular moments" that occur often prove to be the most important. This process will be intuitive rather than systematic. On the philosophical level, I follow Garred (1996, p. 84) in viewing improvisation as "an intuitive healing process rather than a systematic intervention process". I anticipate, however, that intuition itself may be perceived as a methodological technique on a practical level and thus appear to be a systematic intervention, even if the intention was different. This type of argument is always challenging because verbalizing implies so many separate and interdependent levels at the same time.

I see joint music making and joint music listening experiences as emergent meetings between client, therapist, and music—in a *lived space*. The client and the therapist dwell in the aesthetics of the felt musical spatiality, as music itself has spatial dimension.

The music therapy relationship, then, offers great potential in itself. The musical moving-along process allows for dichotomies such as closeness-distance, predictability-unpredictability, spontaneity-rigidity, complementarity-equality, and subject-object positions. In such an exploration, the musical process cannot be predicted, nor can the perception and the experience of music. In a conversation afterwards, something is verbalized, but something will remain implicit. I do apprehend, however, joint music making and music listening experiences as immediate relationships in themselves. The music therapist might use different techniques in the relationship (Bruscia, 1987). However, *how* these techniques are used and perceived in the musical processes is most important. I agree with Garred's (2006) contention that improvisation (and, I would add, a joint music listening experience) is a method within music therapy that can be perceived as an encounter. At the same time, such an encounter cannot be simplified to a method. The immediacy itself characterizes the sense of being together. In this way, musical improvisation and music listening experiences present a paradox in practice; they both become a means of attaining immediacy.

To take an example from expressive music therapy, consider a client who expressed her or his joy while playing a drum. Within the musical improvisation, the client initiates gestures and rhythm, which are recognized and included in the music therapist's playing. At a detailed level, the client syncopates rhythms while singing and playing on the drum. The therapist picks up these syncopations and captures these musical gestures on the piano. Although the music therapist in this context follows up on the client's initiative, both are at the same time mutually dependent on each other to maintain and develop the musical interaction. In this way, each person's action is displayed to the other, and together they form a unit. The interaction works as a mutual causality.

In a receptive approach, there is a similar process. In a self-listening procedure (Bruscia 2014a), for example, the client(s) and the music therapist listen to a recording of an improvisation, performance, or composition, reflecting on themselves and on the experience. After such listening, one possible approach is to explore the experience verbally. Alternatively, the client(s) and the music therapist may collaborate in choosing the next piece of music to listen to. Accordingly, the client(s) and the music therapist explore a joint but not identical "self-listening" experience.

In music therapy, though, the music therapist quite often, but not always (Lee, 1996), possesses a musical expertise beyond that of the client. It may be easy to assume that this fact might cause a subject-object positioning in the interaction. My experience is that difference in musical skills does not necessarily lead to a subject-object positioning in, for example, a musical improvisation. Ruud (1990) observed that improvisation "allows for flexible transitions between symmetric and complementary connections" (p. 311, my translation). The term *complementary connection* refers to one part governing the improvisation (being the subject), while the other is being led and adapts to the interplay. This is often the case in an interaction where the two partners have large differences in expertise. In a symmetric connection or relationship, there is another balance in the communication, which leads to a greater variety as to who is subject and object in the musical communication. Ruud (p. 311) continued:

> Analysis of improvisations in music therapy can show that there is a great flexibility to change position from object to subject. It lies in the very nature of improvisation that there is a reciprocal exchange of musical ideas. The communication chain is unbroken, and we see no simple stimulus-response chain but a complex feedback pattern where participants' answers always include and presuppose reactions to the other's move, which in turn presupposes, etc.

Therefore, one does not observe a constant subject-object relationship, even when there is a difference in musical skills between the participants in the musical improvisation. It is quite often difficult to realize who is the subject and who is the object of an improvisation. Sometimes one leads, sometimes the other. Paradoxically, improvisations can be mutual and equal at a practical level as well.

In a music listening procedure, such as GIM, the client may have more in-depth knowledge about certain musical pieces than the music therapist. Such a knowledge may actually pose a challenge to the potential music experience in the here-and-now. One client remarked that his knowledge of the score and the orchestral performance reduced his GIM experience, because he was not able to surrender to the music as he wanted to. Another was astonished at how a piece of music that he knew very well transcended his prior experience. "New rooms" with many layers opened up within the GIM experience. He related this extension of rooms and layers to both the music itself and his emotional and mental capacity.

I recognize the client is not the only one who profits from a shift between subject and object in an improvisation or a listening procedure. On the contrary, such an exchange offers therapeutic potential from the therapist's point of view as well. The music therapist cannot be fully aware at all times. Precisely for this reason, it is necessary and useful for the music therapist to switch between a subject and an object position. The music therapist is thus given a space to recede in order to analyze and partake in a reciprocating way as a fellow traveler within the musical relationship.

From a theoretical point of view, such an exchange between positions implies that the aim of the musical interactions is not continuously intersubjective meetings, either verbally or musically— a point also made by Garred (2006). On the contrary, the most important feature is a transformative movement between uncoordinated sequences ("interactive errors") and coordinated sequences ("interactive repairs"), to restore the connection where it is broken (Tronick, 1989). In short, the development of the improvisation and the music listening experience require sensitive adjustment and attunement to allow for recognition of shared experiences at an existential level.

In music therapy practice, the music therapist has the overall responsibility for framing the interaction, while maintaining an overview of the situation. This is not meant to reduce the mutual influence. However, due to the different roles, being the therapist implies a double responsiveness, as the therapist holds the main responsibility for the therapeutic setting. For example, the therapist must not only express herself through music but also look beyond herself. She attunes respectfully to the client through music as she follows and facilitates, allowing the power of music to enable self-expression and communication. The therapist is constantly aware of the other's and her own musical initiative in the present moment. The goal is to try, through her own empathic imagination, to see the situation from the other's perspective while also maintaining her own base (mentalization). The client and music therapist, naturally, do not have the same kind of relationship with each other, because this is primarily not the therapist's process, but the client's. Nevertheless, even though the relationship within the music therapy practice itself is not symmetrical, mutuality is its basis.

In the musical relationship, the therapist and client have different voices due to their mental and physical differences, as well as (in most cases) the difference between their instrumental skills. Mutual recognition and intersubjectivity, however, abolish the need to mark independence and differences. Mutual recognition makes rigor adjustable (Schibby, 1996).

A musical relationship involves creativity. Daring to be present in all we do promotes creation and therefore pleasure. The prize of creativity, however, is always vulnerability. Being creative is always about being brave. When we allow our personality to be visible in what we do, we always take a risk. According to Hellsten (2011), creativity always involves challenging the present structures and daring to think and act in new ways. There is always a certain heroism in real creativity. Creativity promotes a new and different level of courage.

A music therapy relationship offers personal participation so that we can express ourselves in different modes. Musical creativity shows us that we are all vulnerable. It does demystify disorders, as the borders between "normal" and "abnormal" are not given within a musical experience. Music therapy can be life-giving and can offer hope (Aldridge, 1991). A musical experience supports a link between inner and outer space while allowing for appreciative recognition at an existential level; hence, it is a creative health resource that supports life itself.

Music therapy then, is an art form, observable during an improvisation and/or a music listening experience. The deepest nature of art (here music) is inscrutable and linked to human existence. Music as an art form is multidimensional, alive, and created in a participating here-and-now. Seen from an artistic perspective, expressive and receptive music experiences are ambiguous, multilayered phenomena unfolding in time and space, yet paradoxically not bounded by these characteristics. Music allows for a variety of experiences at different levels while supporting the creation of new life stories. The phenomenal music therapy relationship then emerges as an art form—a field of relational lived experiences—emerging from an inborn, communicative musicality.

Chapter 10

The Relational Music Therapist

An *alliance in therapy* refers to the engagement between the individuals in the setting and is usually associated with a positive outcome in therapy. Several terms are used to elucidate such a phenomenon between a music therapist and a client. Examples include therapeutic alliance, working alliance, music alliance, or helping alliance. An alliance may have emotional or cognitive aspects. It includes meaning at different levels and in a variety of modes. The therapeutic alliance represents a curative aspect, and it may in fact produce this outcome (Ryum & Stiles, 2005). At a practical level, an alliance in therapy means positive bonding between the therapist and the client as they trust and care for each other.

Within relational psychotherapy, there is a focus on the treatment alliance as an interaction and cooperation between therapist and client at a deep level. Bordin (1979) suggests the concept of a working alliance, which includes three features. The first two focus especially on dialogue and negotiation between therapist and client; they are agreement on goals and assignment of tasks. Goals especially refer to the actions that the therapist takes to present herself as available to the client. In addition, the therapist attunes herself to the client's subjectivity in a way that supports the alliance. Directedness is observable, for example, in timing and rhythmic movements as the therapist attunes and adjusts herself to the client's rhythm. The third central feature is the development of bonds, which encompasses mutual trust, acceptance, and confidentiality. Emotional bonds emerge from shared activities and mutual understanding, and from the content of the negotiation between therapist and client.

Therapeutic bonds are seen as a common factor in psychotherapy, embedded in the therapeutic alliance. Research has shown, however, that "common factors" in therapy ("the Dodo Bird verdict") do not provide a cure for everything (Kjøli & Ogden, 2013). Common factors include more than an alliance. They include therapist variables, client variables, transtheoretical strategies and principles of change, and client expectations, in addition to the client–therapist relationship. These transtheoretical principles of change include processes of hope, motivation, positive expectation, and corrective experiences, among others (Nissen-Lie, 2013). Techniques and procedures are conceptually located together, but they include only another level beyond the therapeutic alliance. On this basis, a unity of common factors will explain more of the variance in outcome than the alliance alone would explain.

The therapeutic bond (one common factor) as focused on feelings and emotions may function differently in various treatments, such as short-term dynamic psychotherapy and cognitive therapy (Ulvenes et al., 2012). This factor has additional complicating aspects in both clinical practice and research. In child treatment, for example (Fjermestad, 2011; Johns & Svendsen, 2012), this is due to multiple alliance perspectives stemming from the fact that children rarely initiate treatment themselves and are surrounded by influential systemic contexts.

Most of the interaction between people seems to occur in the implicit and non-verbal domain. In therapy, therefore, it is essential to look closely at the therapeutic alliance, as its qualities are linked to positive results in psychotherapy (Binder et al., 2006). From an intersubjective, developmentally informed perspective, the relation itself is both a frame and a possibility for development and change. It includes an intentional application and use of the relationship (Svendsen, 2016). It is important, however, to underscore that if one argues for total mutuality in a therapeutic relationship, the power of the different positions might not be uncovered in an effective way (Hansen, 2010). The most significant quality to develop in such an alliance is the balance of "errors and repairs" in the therapy (Safran & Muran, 2000). A relational perspective in music therapy implies negotiation between the participants, within both the explicit and implicit domains. As the relational turn draws attention to the relational process itself, the mutual regulation is at stake. It can be argued, though, that it is necessary to experience oneself as separate in order to develop autonomy both emotionally and mentally. In music therapy, the client and the therapist are separated, yet bonded at the same time through music. They have a joint but not identical experience. In this way, music therapy offers a dynamic and working relationship that draws on the client's and the therapist's motivations and resources to engage within the frame and goals of music therapy.

There might be a difference between a therapeutic alliance and a positive relationship. A pragmatic way of looking at such a possible difference is to link the first term to an overall theoretical position, whereas the latter points to the lived relationship in the actual context. As previously stated, a working alliance and common factors are important facets of a therapy session. There are, however, huge personal differences between therapists even within the same treatment method, including in music therapy. Rønnestad (2000) stressed the individual therapist's need to adapt to each client, mobilizing therapeutic skills and engagement in supporting and helping the client with the quality of the therapeutic relationship.

The different *therapist positions* are most often linked to dissimilar forms of therapy, for example, psychoanalysis, humanistic therapy, cognitive therapy, and systemic-oriented therapy. These forms emphasize different aspects of human relationships, such as phenomena of transference, an authentic position, or participation within a family. Therapeutic techniques belong to each form, as illustrated by the interpretation or homework, for example, the therapist as neutral, authentic, directive, or active (Hougaard, 1996). Other terms connected to the role of the therapist include, collaborator, helper, motivator, gardener, teacher, guide, friend, peer, evaluator, fellow traveler, neutral listener, coach, and expert. In my opinion, these directions and methods guide and support theoretical knowledge as well as clinical practice, while also assisting a discourse of therapy.

In music therapy, music therapists attune themselves to the client by choosing a variety of aspects, techniques, and roles to meet the client's need in the best way possible through and in music. I contend that a music therapy position based on *recognition* is a fundamental understanding of a developing relationship. An accepting, empathetic, and confirming attitude, based on insight, understanding, and respect is crucial. Such a therapy position is not only something established inside the therapist, but is visible in the relationship. With Schibby (2009), I believe that a recognizable relation is an indispensable condition for a crossover, transferring development, because it gives room for self-assertion and individuality (autonomy) as well as for connection and confirmation. The client should experience an empathic, respectful, and positive regard that confirms her or his basic value and self-esteem. The client's experience of personal value and positive regard from the therapist will likely be connected to the outcome of therapy (Farber & Lane, 2001). Following this line of argument, the therapist should also be open to the client's transcendent and spiritual experiences, but should never force any spiritual attitude upon the client. Spirituality and religious issues are very often within one's intimate, holy, and private space (Austad, 1996). Respect for the client's integrity and freedom is a basic value in music therapy.

Rogers (1951/1965) outlined some characteristics of a person-centered approach. He offered a briefly stated hypothesis (Rogers, 1979, p. 1) saying:

> It is that the individual has within him or herself vast resources for self-understanding, for altering the selfconcept basic attitudes, and her or his self-directed behaviour—and that these resources can be tapped if only a definable climate of facilitative psychological attitudes can be provided.

Rogers suggested three attitudinal qualities that characterize a person-centered approach as the therapist seeks to create a climate for change. The first element is about genuineness, realness, or congruence. Rogers related these traits to openness and attitudes that are flowing in the moment, or awareness. This attitude resonates with an authentic position. The second has to do with acceptance, caring, or prizing, i.e., an unconditional positive regard. I interpret prizing in this setting as including appreciative recognition. The third aspect of the relationship is to facilitate empathic understanding—a sensitive, active listening, which Rogers claimed is exceedingly rare in our lives. He said that true empathy and real listening are one of the most potent forces for change. Empathy is understood as the therapist's ability and willingness to understand the client's thoughts, feelings, and issues from her or his point of view. Additionally, Rogers emphasized the therapist's relational competencies above technical skills.

A relational perspective on music therapy supports development of change by a deepening and exploration of creative meaning-making within a relational matrix. Dialogue is at the very core, and it comes through a musical relating experience. Aldridge (2000, p. 6) commented:

> The dialogue, which constitutes a sense of coherence of what we are as "selves", is narrative in nature. It is personal and social. If this breaks down then we lose a sense of meaning for ourselves, and we lose meaning as a person in social context.

In music therapy, the narrative and meaning-making can link to a non-verbal and non-semantic level as much as to a semantic and explicit level. It can be a lived story (Stern, 2000), which is stored as an embedded experience at a non-verbal and implicit level.

A working relationship presupposes some *therapist characteristics*. About what kind of music therapist are we talking? Historically, most therapy models have put method and technique over the importance of the therapist as a person (Gelso & Hayes, 2007, cited in Nissen-Lie, 2012).

It seems, however, that the alliance and outcome, in psychotherapy for example, are predicted by the therapist's interpersonal qualities and problems, which also stem from personal relations. "What characterizes good or less good psychotherapists?" Nissen-Lie (2012) asked. Professional qualities like education, further education, experiences, gender, and age seem not to influence very strongly the emergence of a working alliance and the outcome of therapy. Nissen-Lie discovered multifaceted and meaningful links between the therapists' perception of themselves and the outcomes: professional self-doubt (that is denoting doubt about one's professional efficacy) were positively associated with the patient's improvement from therapy.

At a meta-level, these findings may indicate that the effect of psychotherapy is partly due to the intersubjective meeting between the therapist as a person and the patient as a person. In addition, the study results indicate that the therapist's subjectivity plays a vital and active role in the therapy process. These findings have relevant implications for the self-reflection and clinical practice, in addition to training and supervision, of psychotherapists (Nissen-Lie, Monsen, & Rønnestad, 2010), and I would add that they are also directly applicable to music therapists.

A relational perspective on music therapy means sharing of one's life world, striving towards a shared but not identical experience. From this experience, the relationship develops and expands: "The therapist cannot make the necessary change for the client, nor can the therapist force the client to make the necessary changes, no matter how much guidance and motivation are applied" (Bruscia, 2014a, p. 74).

A music therapist has many tasks, among which are to be there for the client, to understand the client's need and resources, to empathize with the client, and to give the client a voice. Additional needs include interacting with the client, holding an anchor (to ground and connect the client to self and world), communicating with the client, and providing opportunities for self-reflection. Moreover, the therapist must present and explore alternatives, guide (and intervene) as necessary, motivate, validate and affirm, care for the client, and protect one's own ability to help (Bruscia, 2014a). In my opinion, these qualifications are important regardless of one's position in the music therapy discourse over whether the therapist is termed a "helper" (Solli & Rolvsjord, 2015).

At a concrete level, the therapist should be able to create a safe enough space to explore the relationship through music, which affords a space of trust. Relationship is always about trust (Grimen, 2009). Through a relating experience in music, the client is invited to explore the feeling that the therapist is useful for her or him. In a relating setting, the therapist stands for a warm and empathic presence, showing herself as trustworthy to the client. The therapist can offer and negotiate toward the creation of an intersubjective field. One characteristic is an "emotional availability" to support not only attachment released by a new phase of the relationship (Bowlby, 1988) but also intersubjective sharing (Malloch & Trevarthen, 2009). Trustworthiness and authenticity seem to be important characteristics (Trondalen, 2004b).

In a semi-structured interview, I asked one client after completion of therapy (Trondalen, 2004a, p. 283):

> *Th: Do you think that your relationship to me has influenced your music therapy?*
> Cl: It is security, in a way. That's what it is. You see, if I don't feel I'm able to accomplish so much musically, there is a person there to do so, so in a way I feel I can be myself with that person. It isn't so dangerous to be sad. It is a pillar of safety, sort of. ... It is important for me to say I feel safe being with you. It is a pillar to rest upon.

Implicit knowing is vital in the communication between client and therapist in the here-and-now. In an interview, Stern (in Heje & Johansen, 1990) described the attunement process as the pillar of intersubjectivity, while the dynamic forms of vitality are the cornerstones. Stern suggested that it is not interpretation per se that works, but something else; attunement is important because it is the developmental reality of the empathic understanding in the therapeutic relationship. In another interview 16 years later, Stern was asked (in Schanche & Binder, 2006, p. 954; my translation):

> *Int: What would you say when it comes to practicing relational psychoanalysis?*
> Stern: I think experience is necessary to practice in a good way. You rely on yourself and your personal life experience. The practice has to be based on experiences. If I were to choose a therapist, I would choose one who displays certain characteristics.
> *Int: What characteristics would you look for?*
> Stern: It is hard to describe them, but one important

qualification is the ability to attune to other people. I would consider how it felt to be with them. To attune, to follow the other is crucial. Nothing in your CV would tell if you have this quality. There is a clear parallel between a therapist's way of attuning and a mother's ability to attune to her infant.

Relationship matters. According to Haugsgjerd, Jensen, and Karlsson (1998, p. 172), "The power of change lies in the relationship that emerges." This quotation is place under the heading, "The Relationship as a Healing Power." The authors described the attachment process that occurs in such a relationship. They pointed out that the therapist must dare to see herself as important to the patient during the process of therapy. Such a standpoint is encouraging and a reminder of the importance of a real and attuned encounter with oneself and the other. In other words, the therapist should have an authentic interest in other people, while always thinking, "I wonder whether ... ," since the therapist, philosophically speaking, can never know the depths of another person. Bruscia (2014a, p. 284) stated:

Being holistic is an ideal that is impossible to ever accomplish. Therapists simply do not have the ability to understand all of a client's needs and potential remedies. Certainly we can strive to conceive of persons in their wholeness and as comprehensively as possible, but as soon as we presume success, that we have in fact thought of and taken care of everything that the person needs, we run the risk of inauthenticity—in all likelihood, we have not perceived or accomplished all that we thought we did.

The aim in an intersubjective approach is to support the client in returning to her or his *personal* line of development. Accordingly, the therapist needs theoretical knowledge to understand developmental processes in a broad therapeutic context. The therapist would need to handle a variety of acceptable responses in order to allow for co-creation of meaning. A sensitive presence, awareness of oneself and the other, movement, and vitality within the relationship come into play. Included in these processes are timing, intuition, and emotional togetherness, expressed through implicit and non-verbal processes (Brautaset, Egebjerg, & Johns, 2012). In music therapy, this involves activating an exploratory attitude and a sensitive awareness through communicative musicality (Malloch & Trevarthen, 2009).

I would suggest that being *intuitive* is included in the reflexive task of being a music therapist. Intuition and rationality are sometimes seen as opposites, but I do not think that they are. Husserl observed that intuition is neither mysterious nor difficult to grasp and perceive (in Sokolowski, 1974/1989, p. 26-27): "Intuition is simply consciousness of an object in its direct presence; it is the opposite of intending the object absently. ... There is nothing solipsistic or mysterious about intuitions, and in principle they can be publicly manifest and confirmed." Intuition connects to concrete musical participation (expressive or receptive) and the actions taken in that participation. At the same time, intuition is also directed toward the client and the relationship itself emerging in music therapy. I think the cognitive appraisal of music therapy in action is not cognition in itself, but closer to intuition, as it is an immediate awareness emerging from the music therapist's consciousness.

One way of looking at intuition on a theoretical level is to talk about an "old hand" as opposed to a "beginner's hand." An "old hand" develops through practice the ability to be present musically, therapeutically, and personally, as an active listener and participant at the same time. Such a present awareness includes two components: attending and listening (Eide & Eide, 1996). Attending means being aware and present with the client, while listening connects to observation and interpretation of the client's experience of herself or himself. In clinical practice, the music therapist's choices of methodology and procedures in the session are informed by her immediate, affectively attuned awareness, with its inherent tacit knowledge (empathy, professional skills, experience, and intuition), which is perceived and performed in the here-and-now (Trondalen, 2013c).

In sum, intuition in music therapy is an immediate and creative mobilization of the total and unified experience that the music therapist possesses.

Self-care

Connections make us stronger and vulnerable at the same time. This is indeed true in an *intersubjective* perspective on relational music therapy. Self-care, in the present setting, means caring for oneself as a music therapist so that one can care for others.

Music therapists need to find joy in a meaningful (professional) working life so that they can support their clients, developing and sustaining themselves throughout their lifetime. Music therapists need to work on their personal weaknesses and strength to be able to interact with the client as a "good-enough mother" (Winnicott, 1971, p. 11). Self-care means giving to oneself as well as receiving care and support from others. Useful self-caring actions can be performed through music (Hanser & Mandel, 2010; Loewy & Hara, 2007) and other practices (Waldman & Clark, 2013; Richards, 2007; Trondalen, 2016b).

The music therapist has many roles in her life, such as clinician, musician, researcher, supervisor, mentor, and teacher, often in addition to family obligations. Mental health is a balancing act influenced by genes, traumas, private pressures, and professional stress (Beck, 2012). As members of a helping profession, music therapists may also experience burnout (Hills, Norman, & Forster, 2000; Richardson-Delgado, 2006; Vega, 2010), compassion fatigue (Figley, 2002), or compassion stress (Gerbert, 2010; Glomb, 2007; Montello, 2000). It is thus essential for the music therapist to identify needs and resources in her own life. Obviously, self-care has to be linked to the music therapist's context in a broad sense.

Working as a *music therapist* means being in the world together with a client or a group. Conducting music therapy sessions is mentally demanding and time-consuming, and perhaps the music therapist sometimes misses the joint nurturing of being present in the relating experience per se. Improvising, listening, composing, and talking together—all these elements constitute the power of the present moment and may actually afford self-care for the music therapist as well. Through being open-minded and present in the moment, the "most unexpected and unpredictable things may emerge, which may be the most interesting," according to Stern (in Schanche

& Binder, 2006, p. 1263). While engaging with the client at a genuine level, the music therapist is also vitalized in the musical relationship. Experiencing meaningfulness as a therapist, in terms of contributing to personal growth, is both a consequence of and a contributor to effective therapeutic involvement. The link between the experience of therapeutic work and one's work ethic seems to affect one's ongoing professional development. The emergence of demoralization, in terms of experienced decline in the therapy process, is a precursor and a consequence of stress (Rønnestad & Orlinsky, 2006).

The music therapist is also a *musician* (Trondalen, 2013c). "Music isn't something that I do; it's something that I am" (Richardson-Delgado, 2006, p. 84). Ongoing development of musical skills is important to a music therapist. Performing music in a band or orchestra, singing in a choir, and listening to music may nurture the musician in her daily life. Music therapists most often have important musical narratives forming their pathway toward music therapy (Bonde et al., 2013; Trondalen, 2013c). In an article concerning improvisation, Bildung, and therapy, Hegi (2015, p. 120, my translation)[2] said, "As a musician myself, I have had this basic experience; improvisation offers amazing potential for healing through self-awareness, in the dynamics of a relationship, and as freedom from constraints."

Music and musicianship offer wonderful experiences, often leading to the experience of wholeness and healing (Gabrielson, 2011). Even though music therapy and music performance make many demands and takes their toll, as the title "*Mich macht krank, was ich liebe*" (What I love makes me ill) (Decker-Voigt, 2012) indicates, music therapists and musicians can benefit from music as a means of self-care, using it to nurture themselves, balance their emotions, and develop new strength (Trondalen, 2016a). However, even this might be threatening if the joy of music making or listening to music is diminishing due to work that is emotionally and mentally draining.

The treatment of burnout among musicians and music therapist

---

2. Original text: "Ich habe als Musiker selber die Urerfahrung gemacht, welch unerhörtes Heilpotential in der Improvisation liegt: als Selbsterfahrung, als Beziehungsdynamik und als Befreiung von Zwängen."

are often difficult to identify, as they most often are treated in relation to their medical condition (Bradt, Dileo, & Portvin, 2013; Bradt & Dileo, 2014; Dileo, 2015). Compassion fatigue may be as scary to a music therapist as to a professional musician, as it may have a direct effect on one's professional career as a music therapist. A variety of studies on the experience of being an injured musician confirm that illness and stress threaten the musician's existential being (Buller, 2002; Montello, 2003). Research studies indicate that receptive music therapy reduces chronic stress and performance anxiety (Martin, 2007; McKinney, Antoni, Kumar, Tims, & McCabe, 1997). Case studies also indicate positive benefits of music therapy with musicians, in both private and institutional settings (Austin, 2006; Decker-Voigt, 2012).

A music therapist might also be a *teacher and a researcher* with academic obligations, often in addition to clinical work. Despite their daily pressures, music therapy faculty experienced significantly less burnout than the normative sample in the Maslach Burnout Inventory (Richardson-Delgado, 2006). Music therapy faculty possess resources that other professionals might not have, such as the ability to find rejuvenation through music. One interviewee (Richardson-Delgado, 2006, p. 84) said, "I think that we forget as music therapists to take care of our own music and take care of ourselves through music ... you know, it's the whole reason we got into this thing in the first place."

Doing research, teaching, and working in music therapy practice allow for an in-depth investigation of clinical, theoretical, and philosophical levels of music therapy. Even though these activities may be time-consuming and exhausting, they also lead to deeper knowledge, promoting personal, clinical, and scientific integration (Trondalen, 2004b). Many music therapists use their spirituality as a resource in their clinical work, and music is intrinsically linked with the spiritual for many persons (Pethybridge, 2013). One faculty member reported, "I also pray. I mean it's part of my religious belief and so, when I'm feeling stressed and like I can't handle things I pray about it" (Richardson-Delgado, 2006, p. 86).

Self-experience is of vital importance in a relational approach to music therapy. Working as a music therapist means linking personal competence, musicality, personality, and theoretical and existential orientation. Such an integrative task implies working on personal narratives at different levels (Engedal, 2003). In accordance with Stern's belief (in Schanche & Binder, 2006), self-experience is necessary to practice an intersubjective experience in relational (music) therapy, as the therapist relies on her personal life experience in so many respects. Such a view also resonates with the need for "professional self-doubt" (Nissen-Lie, 2012) in terms of exploration and reflection at a personal level as a music therapist.

Music therapists are, like other people, wounded through life experiences. Exploring the wounded healer within oneself may be liberating and may afford new possibilities of action for the music therapist herself (Wolgien & Coady, 1997). This is also in accordance with the daily saying, "What you don't know does something with you. What you do know means you can act yourself." Exploring personal wounds and strengths through self-experience empowers the therapist and makes her strong in a vulnerable way. Being consciously aware of these processes allows for the exploration of intersubjectivity in a whole range of ways.

One concrete way of performing self-experience is to play out a "Musical Life Panorama" (MLP) alone or together with others:

> The MLP works with the emotional meaning of experiences, events and memories that are connected with music in one's biography and it can be used in a verbal form (talking about music) and in an active form (conducting improvisation). (Frohne-Hagemann, 1998, p. 104)

The self-experience may also serve as a musical memory album, opening up opportunities for the music therapist's development and growth (Trondalen, 2013a, 2016b).

Supervision is an important part of a self-care process for a relational music therapist. Supervision can be performed verbally or on the basis of different music therapy methods such as improvisation, composing, and song writing and then elaborated in a conversation afterwards (Forinash, 2001; Odell-Miller & Richards, 2008; Pedersen, 2013). According to Bruscia (2014a, p. 90), "Supervision and consultation with other therapists are two excellent ways to safeguard oneself against compassion fatigue and burnout. In addition, music therapists have another powerful resource—the ability to nurture themselves musically."

GIM is a useful supervision tool, as the model offers a multilayered modality for investigating professional issues. A time-limited agreement (Johns & Svendsen, 2016; Trondalen, 2009–2010) on supervision can be useful for investigating a limited range of topics. This was the case with Susan, a music therapist who was supervised through five GIM sessions. Susan found it hard to believe that she was good enough and thus struggled to promote herself in her daily music therapy job. During her GIM journey, Susan connected to the deep bass tones in the music, to her inner strength, while exploring her personal ambivalence about trusting in herself through different images. She encountered an old man encouraging her to stand up and believe in herself. Susan titled her drawing of the GIM journey "Transformation."

This outcome is in line with Pine and Aronson's (1988) suggestion that draining feelings of powerlessness begin to recede when the person begins to take responsibility for promoting change in a difficult situation. Allowing oneself time and space to receive individual supervision opens up exploration of sensitivity and awareness and an investigation of personal strengths and weaknesses. It permits an exploration of presence through affective dialogues at a micro level. Such a presence links to the therapist's personal agency (Brautaset, Egeberg, & Johns, 2012).

Group supervision, which can also encompass creative arts other than music, is relevant and useful for music therapists to exchange ideas and learn from each other, while receiving responses related to oneself as a music therapist. Using music and lyrics can inspire and promote development in both the individual and the supervision group. Group supervision can affect every individual and deepen the process of belonging to a group of peers. Music therapy faculty members have emphasized the importance of supervision and mentoring programs (Richardson-Delgado, 2006).

Working as a music therapist involves encountering existential themes as well. For example, music therapists working within a palliative end-of-life setting (Dileo & Loewy, 2005) or with people who have threatening illnesses would need inspiration and integration to offer the best possible therapy approach. Pastoral or philosophical counseling could address existential themes through music or in verbal communication. Existential experiences, including those that come through music, connect to all of the questions and wonderments that are part of being human.

Clinical supervision and self-experience are rated as the second or third most important experience for professional development, following clinical work experience with patients. An international study (N = 7,000 from 24 countries) on psychotherapists' work and professional development drew attention to what is termed a double traumatization. The same phenomenon arises in music therapy supervision when the supervisee experiences stress with the supervisor in addition to stress with clients. A vicious circle may develop: stress is enhanced by negative supervision, and negative processes are worsened by stress-characterized involvement with patients. Therefore, the supervisor must be especially attentive regarding the risk of double traumatization when the supervisee experiences stress-related involvement with her patients. The supervisor should be able to repair errors in the alliance with the supervisee in a constructive and supportive way (Rønnestad & Orlinsky, 2006). As unexperienced therapists are most vulnerable, professional development—particularly through supervision—is important as it can reduce the negative effects of stress-related therapeutic involvement.

A music therapist has to deal with all feelings, either overt or hidden. It is important to uncover and relate to such phenomena as shame. Many conditions, such as eating disorders (Trondalen, 2015, 2016c), substance abuse, and reactions to violation and abuse, carry with them the intoxicating power of shame, which may affect the client as well as the music therapist. Supervision offers the music therapist a necessary exploration of a variety of underlying affects connected to self-esteem.

Chapter 11

Life World Existentials: Themes Of Meaning

Philosophically, we experience the body from an inside perspective, as the body is intentional and always directed toward something. The relationship between the individual and the surroundings expresses itself through two different philosophical movements prevalent in the 20th century. These are the bodily turn and the the linguistic turn, which ascribe the relationship between the subject and the world to ontological and epistemological status, respectively. The bodily turn links to phenomenology and hermeneutics, as the bodily subject constitutes itself through its contact with the world. The linguistic turn, meanwhile, is associated with social constructivism and discourse analysis, while understanding the relationship between the body and the world as linguistically constituted. The body is a *carrier* of subjectivity, while language *produces* subjectivity (Holgersen, 2006).

The bodily turn takes an interpretative phenomenological position concerning the "body-self." It does, however, take into account that some element of interpretation and context is always involved at a practical level, due to the tension between the two philosophical positions. These positions may not merge in a direct and straight way. Inspired by Van Manen's chapter on "Hermeneutic Phenomenological Reflections" (1990), I recognize that the project of phenomenological reflections and understanding is dealing with the experience as lived, whereas I, as a music therapist, attempt to grasp the therapeutic essence of a certain musical relating experience. The musical relating experience is the lived experience as it emerges in the here-and-now in music therapy. As a music therapist, I recognize meaning to be multidimensional and multilayered. Meaning in music therapy, then, can never be perceived and expressed in a single (essential) definition. On this basis, interpretative phenomenology is one useful way of dealing with the tension between these two positions, particularly with regard to procedural efforts within a musical and interpersonal analysis of music therapy as practice.

Following this position, themes of meaning link to *life world existentials* (themes of meaning) as guides to reflection. These existentials include the *lived body* (corporeality), *lived space* (spatiality), *lived time* (temporality), and *lived human relation* (relationality or communality). These four fundamental existentials of a life world "belong to the existential ground by way of which all human beings experience the world, although not all in the same modality of course" (Van Manen, 1990, p. 102). We even experience different life worlds at different times of the day. These four existentials can be differentiated but not separated, as they have been considered as belonging to the fundamental structure of the lifeworld.

The first theme of meaning linked to life world existentials is the *lived body* (corporeality). It refers to a phenomenological position, stating that we are always in the world as intentional beings. We are experiencing the body from an inside perspective, and our beings are always directed toward something, be it an imagination or an artefact. Our body self and consciousness are embedded in the perception of our general being. Therefore, the body is the starting point for any phenomenological perception. At the same time, we experience the body from an outside perspective, and as a living body within the world. Human beings are intersubjectively available to each other through the phenomenal human body. From a philosophical point of view, this phenomenal living and thinking body is able to perceive and grasp at the same time (Merleau-Ponty, 1962).

With reference to Damasio (2000), Sletvold (2005, p. 497) stated, "In the beginning was the Body." He argued that awareness of the emotional body state was a prerequisite for rational thinking. The body embeds thoughts and eventually language. The tension between body as felt and body as a container of an emergent language makes a joint effort in the body itself. The thoughts dwell in the body (Polanyi, 1969) while also emerging in a relationship with other people. We become ourselves through bodily expressions while encountering and opening ourselves to the other.

A form of circularity takes place, and reflection and action are thus not separate entities, but neither do they completely merge. It seems, though, that *movement* is the phenomenon that best describes such an intertwining. It is within the movement itself that an eventual fixed thought or body dissolves. Within such a movement, the body opens up to a concrete interplay between inner and outer dimensions, as the body self accommodates a proper balance between physical, mental, and existential aspects of the human being. This is similar to Stern's (2010) focus when exploring vitality. The body is an experiencing subject, not only a tool for the consciousness. In contrast to a body-mind dualism, the human being is one whole. The body is perceptive, expressive, and capable of memory.

Language, then, may function as a double-edged sword. Even though language allows for sharing of inner worlds and narratives, it "drives a wedge" (Stern, 2000, p. 162) between the body experience as lived and body experience as verbally narrated. This is indeed evident in music therapy as music making and listening to music are immediate and non-verbal processes, immediate and sensed lived experiences, that remain in the body, whereas talking about one's experience in music therapy is a verbal, reflective, and mediated process. From an ontological point of view, the distant relationship to the world may be seen as an illusion because we are present in the body within every perception of the world as beings.

The human being is neither consciously separate from the body in a dualistic way nor purely a biological organism. The living body is a body subject, an experiencing body self, and it is in relation to other body selves (Johansson, 2009). When two such subjects meet, we can talk about inter-bodiness. The experience that these two bodies make together is stored as memories and forms a part of our body biography (Eckhoff, 1997a, 1997b; Loos, 1994). Such experiences may include early dialogical interplay with close intimate others and may be restored as good memories. Others have experienced extremely negative bodily experiences—for example through offenses of diverse types (Kim, 2015; Moffitt & Hall, 2003–2004; Rogers, 1995). All experiences influence the development of a body self while also linking to the individual's body logic as defined by the individual perception of life. In music therapy practice, it is evident that such a view includes a great sensitivity to the person's experienced bodily boundaries, where physical distance and bodily closeness are two sides of the same coin.

We could take various illnesses as illustrative examples. When one is suffering from an eating disorder, eating and food are at the forefront. Food and the body appear to be primary to the client. At the same time, the body is secondary when it is used as a concrete medium for an inner life, i.e., embodiment (Duesund & Skårderud, 2003). The body becomes subject and object at the same time. The living and perceiving body becomes the absent body (Leder, 1990). Another example would be a musician where the body is linked to a personal and professional identity: an injured shoulder leads to pain, reduced practice time, and probably a stiffer performance. This biological challenge might result in sick leave and/or depression, either of which threatens the musician's ability to pursue her or his career (particularly as a freelancer).

When we are burdened by illness or injury, our confidence in our own self-agency and ability to act is shaken (Pihl, 1989/2009). The flutist Buller (2002, p. 22) described what it is like to be an injured musician: "It's painful; it's as if my familiar self and world has died." When illness and trauma threaten to remove our connections to familiar events and experiences in our lives, they threaten our existential being (Schei, 2009). Interestingly, brain research and neuroscience today have exposed the connections between inner muscles, basic physiological processes, and mental functioning, particularly in the context of slow movement techniques and methods (for example, Pilates, Feldenkreis, or Qi Gong). Slow movements seem to promote an increased intake of oxygen (Sparre, 2009a; von der Fehr, 2008). In particular, the limbic system and thalamus—"the brain's neurophysiological Me" (Sparre, 2009b, p. 9)—provide a "link between the cortex and the brain stem, which might have a central role in connecting emotional tonus and mood" (Myskja & Lindbæk, 2000, p. 1184). It thus appears that the cognitive neuron networks are very important to the adequate regulation of our emotions (Blood, Zatorre, Bermundez & Evans, 1999; Plessen & Kabricheva, 2010). When musicians or clients grow nervous and display physical symptoms during a performance or music therapy session, the body is talking (Trondalen, 2004a, 2013c).

The second theme of meaning linked to life world existentials is the *lived space* (spatiality). We most often talk about space through dimensions such as length, height, depth, and distance, for example, the spatial dimensions of a house, in mathematical terms. The lived space, however, is not so easily grasped through language, as the experience of lived space is largely pre-verbal—a phenomenon on which we generally do not reflect. Lived space is felt space. The space that we inhabit always influences how we feel, whether in a music therapy setting or in life in general. Walking in the mountains with a clear horizon may make us feel small; improvising with a client who plays an endless line of notes with no breaks or variations in dynamics may prompt the feeling of limited space for the music therapist. "In general, we may say that we become the space we are in," said Van Manen (1990, p. 102). "Lived space is the existential theme that refers us to the world or landscape in which human beings move and find themselves at home."

The nature of the lived space is interesting. Linking to music therapy, the body space has an existential and physical dimension, which is important in both music making and listening to music. The nature of the space we offer the client when playing music does matter to the experience of space to explore oneself in music therapy. The client and the therapist inhabit the spatiality of the room physically, psychosocially, bodily, and musically. The aesthetics of the lived space in music therapy matters as well. Lived space has both cultural and personal qualities. Growing up in cultural and social conventions where one is usually granted little space affords different experiences from growing up in a culture with unlimited space. In addition, different personalities react differently to closeness versus distance when encountering people.

Music itself has spatial dimensions. We talk about music in a high or low pitch, saying that the music moves up or down, or becomes loud or quiet. Sounds and timbre can be close or distant. Loud or deep sound images can be compact and condensed or spread out and easy to grasp. Music is "a virtual time-space" (Christensen, 2012, p. 105). Terms like crescendo and diminuendo, piano and forte point to special phenomena in space. Sound dwells in spatiality.

As human beings, we experience and perceive groups of

elements as interactions of foreground and background components in spatiality, most often as gestalts. We organize, choose, and select sounds based on subjective curiosity and directedness. The music or sounds we experience through our senses have a basis in aesthetical preferences and perceptive stimuli. These senses assimilate what stands out in contrast to others. They establish priority interests and form different preferred paths of events (Kruse, 2016). These different priority levels allow for an exploration of interactive expressive potentials. Following that, a dialogue between foreground and background elements, as dynamic forces, comes into play. Time and space in the creating process itself are evident, as they are important in the procedural dialogue between the client and the music therapist.

There seems to be no such thing as a completely empty space, neither in life nor in music therapy. In music therapy, silence is indeed evident to allow the improvising partners to act (Sutton, 2003). One question emerges: how is it actually for a client to be "alone" in the silence within a music therapy improvisation or in a music listening experience? Being left in spatiality may function as an invitation to act. At the same time, the feeling of being alone may also occur and lead to the opposite of acting. In this way, spatiality influences the ability to perform self-agency in a musical improvisation. Pauses and breaks, syncopations and restrained expressions are all spatial qualities that allow for experiences of the music as vivid and vibrant, and as a phenomenon in which to dwell and act in the present space.

The third theme of meaning linked to life world existentials is *lived time* (temporality). The dimensions of lived time are always present in music and in life in general. We are born into life, and we disappear out of measurable time. There are different views on how the nature of lived time links to our temporal way of being in the world. To a young person, life seems to be never-ending, whereas elderly people tend to experience life with a limited future, recollecting the past. "The temporal dimensions of past, present, and future constitute the horizon of a person's landscape" (Van Manen, 1990, p. 104).

Every life and every therapy session has its boundaries, provided by time. Time is the "the fourth dimension in integration," according to Winnicott (1961, in Davis & Wallbridge, 1981/2011, p. 169). He connected time to the existential experience of continuity of

112

one's life course. A break in continuity could affect one's ability to connect the past with the present and eventually make it hard to imagine the effects of the present upon the future. Time and process give form and meaning to life. Winnicott observed that in time, the end is in sight from the beginning. Time is evident within all therapy processes and within the musical experiences themselves. The duration of the therapy process, in terms of number of sessions and months, is also significant. Time functions as an organizing principle in therapy. We know, every music therapy process ends, and still the parting is fragile (Kim, 2014; Trondalen, 2001). In sum, every life and every music therapy service has time boundaries.

The phenomenology of time is experienced through *chronos* and *kairos*, or objective and subjective perceptions of time, respectively. Kairos refers to a conceptualization of time that is personal rather than public—one in which "time is in a state of flux; it is concerned with flexibility and the convergence of multiple tasks. Time is seen as springing from the self" (Aldridge, 1996, p. 37). During such an experience of flux, in music or in life, objective time fades away and the subjective lived experience takes over.

It thus follows that the nature of temporality (lived time) as it structures experience is different from that of chronological time. Husserl's (1964) reference to the streaking comet is appropriate to represent our efforts to understand more of the inner flow of time when we hear a melody. Ferrara (2005, pp. 137) said:

> Husserl utilizes the concepts of retention and protention to describe the inner flow of time that occurs when listening to a melody. He uses the metaphor of a comet traveling through space. The glistening tail of the comet represents past notes of the melody that have been retained in immediate memory. The present is represented by the head of the comet, and the trajectory or "projectory" of the comet is analogous to "protending" or predicting where the melody might lead or be developed. During any "now" instant or point in a melody, notes heard earlier are retained in consciousness while one anticipates further development and closure.

When we listen to music, we hear a melody as a unit. We do not hear successive and dislocated notes. The melody appears to us as a whole, while being constituted by consciousness in time. Similarly, we can for example anticipate being at stage doing a musical performance. We can 'feel' the experience and 'hear' the music, even if we do not perform in the actual moment. As one musician Tea, said during her GIM journey, "I am playing, changing between cello and violin ... I've never played the cello before ... it's very convincing, brilliant vibrato and a 'schwung' ('vital momentum') of the stroke." (Trondalen, 2016a, p. 12). Anticipation is not about conscious thinking, but links to what emerges (directs) from ourselves. Such an anticipation, however, will always be a reduction ('constrain'), as all perception links to what actually reaches us in the here and now.

> As one progresses through a melody (or work), protentions (future notes or phrases) become less and less protensive, then become present as "now" points and finally recede into the past. Perhaps most important is that during this entire experience of musical time, one experiences a melody (and an entire work) as one enduring whole. (Ferrara, 2005, p. 137).

Transferred to music playing and music listening in music therapy, every 'now' includes both what has been and an anticipation of what is emerging. Every 'now', is perceived not as divided units but is included as a whole. Hence, the whole music is vivid in memory as a unified unit. The duration of the moment then, links to earlier experience, action, and anticipated interplay.

Consciousness intends or directs its awareness towards things in time. Polkinghorne (1989, p. 43) comments that, "consciousness is intentional in the sense that an essential characteristic of experience is that it is always an experience of something. Consciousness is an activity guided by human intention rather than determined by mechanical causation." Accordingly, there is not necessarily an intention in terms of motivated directedness, as is proposed from a psychological perspective (Stern, 2000)

Past, present and future link to each other in a "now." To the client, a significant moment in therapy may mean that the client experienced the moment in a "now," on the basis of an immediate past (retention) and with a certain direction toward the future (protention). Such a process may take place because objects remain the same in consciousness, since (a) they do remain physically in the real world and (b) this anticipation or directedness toward the future is controlled by consciousness as it checks the relationship with previous awareness of the same object (Ferrara, 1984, 2005). In music therapy, this may mean that a client experiences coherence and continuity from the past in such a way that it is possible to experiment rhythmically and affectively in a "now" while still anticipating a (musical) future. Such a view may shed light upon why interplay in music therapy does not necessarily stop or break down when a client experiences sudden breaks or differences in the music relationship.

Stern (2004) also addressed the phenomenon of time, making a connection to the phenomenological terms *retention* and *protention* as he focused on how states of feeling are represented in memory and perception, as subjective experiences characterized by unfolding in time. Stern especially considered the nature of the "present moment," proposing that it has a duration and consists of three parts. The first part is a present-of-the-present-moment, which is not very different from the present instant of *chronos*. The second part is a past-of-the-present-moment, an immediate past that is still echoing at the present instant (retention) similar to the tail of the previously mentioned comet. Stern underscored that retained past is still within the felt presence. The third part is a future-of-the-present-moment (protention), or the immediate and anticipated future. Stern suggests, "the most essential point about this three-part present moment is that all of its parts stand together, subjectively, as a single unified, coherent, global experience occurring in a subjective now." (Stern, 2004, p. 27).

In music, the musical phrase builds on a unitary, coherent form in the mind while it is happening. The reconstruction, elaborations, and embellishment of the music change the experience; however, the reconstruction does not create the phase itself. "And that is the essential point. A coherent experience was grasped during the present moment, even though that experience may have multiple fates" (Stern, 2004, p. 30). This co-experience of the past, present, and future is always linked together, both in present moments in music therapy and in life in general. According to Stern (2004, p. 31), "This trialogue between the past, present and future occurs almost continuously from moment to moment in art, life and psychotherapy."

Structure and continuity are important aspects of therapy processes, in addition to the ability to perform self-agency (Haugvik & Johns, 2008). In music therapy, many clients have experienced broken relationships and disconnected familiar bonds, perhaps as a result of unforeseen past behaviors and events. These experiences may be relived as if experienced in the here-and-now, due to the subjective experience of lived time. Through music therapy's multidimensional nature, the past may be influenced by—and changed through—an emotional presence in a present moment. In music therapy, it is important to work with life themes of disruption and continuation in addition to the ongoing process of errors and repairs in microprocesses in the here-and-now (Tronick, 1989). Time and timing are indeed evident in these processes.

Lived human relation (relationality or communality) is the fourth of the life world themes serving as a guide to reflection. The lived body, lived space, lived time, and lived human relation all belong to the existential ground from which human beings experience the world in different ways. "*Lived other (relationality)* is the lived relation we maintain with others in the interpersonal space that we share with them" (Van Manen, 1990, p. 104). Individuals meet other directly through their bodies—for example, through a handshake or a hug (i.e., in a corporeal way). We also meet other people more indirectly, such as through a book, a photo, or music. Interestingly, these forms of meeting also give us an impression of the other. This anticipation or impression may be confirmed or not confirmed if an actual personal encounter takes place. As human beings, we have the possibility to transcend our selves.

Human beings exist within a relational matrix at different levels and in a variety of settings and contexts. Individuals are searching toward each other through different dimensions. In a broader sense, Van Manen (1990, pp. 105–106) argued, human beings search, through their experience of the other, for "the social sense of purpose in life, meaningfulness, grounds for living." Every relationship is a

116

special lived relationship, highly personal and loaded with interpersonal significance. There is an uncertainty in such living; as human beings, we are bound to each other. Allowing oneself to consciously become involved with another person is never predictable.

From a philosophical point of view, these life conditions are equally valid to the music therapist as to the client. Within a relational paradigm, we are all in the world together. We give each other pleasure and disappointments, comfort or sores. I am dependent upon the other, and the other is dependent upon me. The other is present as a possibility and a responsibility.

Playing in reality

Playing is a phenomenon that unites all four fundamental existentials of a life world, embedding the creative act of taking part—a doing—in a game or a being with other individuals. Playing connects time and space in a similar way to musical playing or music listening; time and space fade away, and subjective time—the "as if"—takes over. Within playing, something new emerges. Playing emerges from and within real life—*in reality*.

Playing consists of dynamic forms, which create different subjective experiences. It is not inner psychic reality. Playing is outside the individual, but it is not the external world either. Winnicott (1971, p. 41) proposed the concept of "potential space," linking it to the area of overlap that may exist between the playing of the mother and that of the child, or between the playing of a therapist and that of a client. Potential space elucidates the creation of an interpersonal and inviting field. The notion implies a safe space, allowing for connectedness to others while playing spontaneously:

> I put forward for the discussion of its value as an idea the thesis that for creative playing and for cultural experience, including its most sophisticated developments, the position is *the potential space* between the baby and the mother (Winnicott, 1971, p. 107).

117

A potential space allows for a three-dimensional experience, in that change (a property of time) can take place. Such an experience transcends the boundaries between inner and outer. Playing is creative and occurs in a temporally and spatially structured place defined by these three dimensions, allowing for a variety of subjective experiences including the cultural experience of music. Winnicott (1971, p. 50) stated, "Playing is an experience, always a creative experience, and it is an experience in the space-time continuum, a basic form of living." I would add that the body (corporality) and the human relation (relationality or communality) are always present as existential soundboards or beings.

In *Playing and Reality*, Winnicott (1971, p. 51) drew attention to significant moments in therapy. He argued that psychotherapy can dig deeply without interpretive work: "... the point that I make in reporting what I call 'therapeutic consultations' [is] that the significant moment is that at which *the child surprises himself and herself.* It is not the moment of my clever interpretation that is significant" (emphasis in original).

A significant moment may occur when the individual "surprises" herself or himself. Of the mutual playing between the patient and the analyst, Winnicott stated, "*This playing had to be spontaneous, and not compliant or acquiescent,* if psychotherapy is to be done" (p. 51). Such a moment does not imply therapeutic interpretation per se. On the contrary, such a moment supports psychotherapy of a deep-going kind without interpretative work. Winnicott (p. 40) argued, then, that playing is just as evident in the analyses of adults as in our work with children, as it "manifests itself for instance, in the choice of the words, in the inflections of the voices, and indeed in the sense of humour."

In music therapy, which is a cultural experience, the client(s) and the music therapist play together as they direct and attune themselves toward the music and the musical participation. Playing deals with joy and fun as deep existential themes are seriously played out during musical playing in different modes. Such a dialogical relationship in music therapy allows for responsiveness, which Stensæth (2008) called musical answerability in her discussion of Bakhtin's dialogical philosophy.

Creativity, hope, and resources link to the experience of

personal meaning within a variety of cultures. Pattern and dialogues are central with regard to the culture's place within psychology, as all individuals and societies make narratives. They describe implicitly the stories that a person or a society tells about themselves and their actions (Bruner, 1975). At the very core of construal of meaning, there is a dialectic and a tension between the ordinary and the unexpected in all cultures.

Jerome Bruner and Daniel N. Stern discussed cultural diversity at the *Norwegian Congress of Psychology 2007* (Kallevik, 2007). They elucidated the question of "what is culture," from the grand notion of culture, to the micro culture in a treatment setting. Culture is neither purely subjective nor only objective. It is contextual and includes ordinariness. "Even in the craziest things we do, the ordinary emerges," Bruner said (Kallevik, 2007, p. 1263, my translation). Stern drew connections from the grand notion of culture to culture in a meeting between a client and therapist: "Whatever you do in the treatment room, everyone contributes to construing a culture. A micro culture. A dialectic culture. How many are needed to share ordinariness? Is two enough, or does it have to be a family?" (p. 1263).

Stern (p. 1263) further argued that there is a need for translation between the individual and the cultural, to a micro level, so that one can grasp and recognize the embodied experience. He elaborated:

> When someone does something that is not usual then the usual becomes visible. ... The most interesting is what emerges from the unexpected and unpredictable ... when we are out of balance and have to think differently. The most interesting is when the therapist stops making notes. (p. 1263)

This is a potent moment—a potential space—where everything is possible. In music therapy, both the ordinary and the unexpected are unveiled. Through a sharing of joint attention, playing and reality emerge through the musical experience. The mother in the music therapy group surprised herself, saying, "I didn't think I could play— but I did." The woman cited earlier in this book listened to her own improvisation and described the music making as her "inner being ...

coming out of prison, so to speak." A man surprised himself, "Wow." (see, chapter 12). Through playful music making and attentive music listening, they were able to surprise themselves. The point is to enter into playing without any presumption or hidden agenda, but with a playful awareness. Time and space cease in the present when unexpected playful experiences link us to the past. Together, we are recreated anew in the moment, supported by hope and an anticipated future through music making and music listening.

To maintain the emotional relationship, timing and presence are core elements in such a surprising and cultural activity. The music therapist and the client need to be in the same vibrant rhythm (at least for some period of time), to allow new experiences or dyadic expanded consciousness of meaning (Lyons-Ruth, 1998) to emerge. Meaning constitutes itself in one's phenomenal musical experience within a culture. Playing is for real.

Chapter 12

Musical Intersubjectivity

Musical intersubjectivity is multifaceted and linked to music as an art form. Music itself is multilayered and ambiguous and offers meaning at different levels and in dissimilar ways. Musical intersubjectivity links to intersubjectivity as a *domain* (of development), an *inborn capacity* and disposition (or "motif"; Trevarthen, 1980)—that is, a relational dimension in itself (an intersubjective matrix, Stern, 2004), as much as a *field* of belonging and acting. Such an intersubjective meaning embeds different layers and a variety of modes. From a philosophical point of view, human beings experience the world in different ways through lived body, lived space, lived time, and lived human relation. These meanings all belong to the existential foundation of life (Van Manen, 1990).

Musical intersubjectivity concerns these shared life world themes. It concerns creating a mental contact. It is about meeting with the other's mind, a joint and shared experience within a relationship that is established through music and interactive in nature. Such a "mental contact" is non-verbal (implicit) and happens within a procedural framework. Musical intersubjectivity links to participation in a moving-along process, from meaningful concrete interplay (for example, improvisation with limited elements) to the ability to create meaning for oneself and others through words (for example, songwriting). This developmental process includes a kind of mental flow, an implicit and procedural knowing, where experience, body, and affects are essential.

The client and the therapist acquire access to each other's life worlds through a shared experience, which may happen in any of the four different interaction formats (Hansen, 2012) and contain different layers in music therapy practice. One format is the sensed attention and synchronization emerging from affective exchange, a face-to-face setting including musical utterances (primary intersubjectivity). Second, musical intersubjectivity might occur inside an advanced improvisation on different instruments as well. The client and the therapist would then each know that the other knew, while the sharing of affects is linked to a shared and joint focus outside themselves (secondary intersubjectivity). Third, musical intersubjectivity may materialize through images, symbols, and narrative within a playful musical communication—for example, through songwriting (Baker, 2015; Baker & Wigram, 2004) or a listening mode like GIM (tertiary intersubjectivity). Lastly, musical intersubjectivity may be observable when one creates a musical based on a personal recovery process, such as the hero's or heroine's journey in GIM. At the very core is the ability to integrate experiences into narratives (tertiary intersubjectivity of second order).

Joint attention, sharing of intentions, and affective states, are all building blocks within intersubjectivity (Trevarthen, 1980). Within a musical intersubjective experience, the client(s) (and the therapist) may experience what inner feeling states can be shared through music. This sharing includes both the form and content of the music and, to the extent possible, a sharing of life worlds. Musical intersubjectivity is primarily about seeing and being aware of, rather than about searching for explicit meaning. Musical intersubjectivity relates to the here-and-now and can be shared without a necessary translation into verbal language, even if the client expresses herself or himself through words on a daily basis. The following example from expressive music therapy, however, includes words as well.

Simen, age 19, had been suffering from bulimia nervosa for about 18 months. Simen went to music therapy for one year, including 19 sessions in an individual outpatient setting (Trondalen, 2004a). At the 17th session, both the client and the therapist knew and talked about the fact that they had only two sessions left. During the previous two sessions, regulation had become a key theme. In fact, at the end of the 15th session, the client had written the word *regulation* within a square. He linked regulation to musical expressions and mutual adjustment in the playing. In addition, we had explored how to perform interpersonal regulation—for example, at parties with friends.

The 17th session included two improvisations. During the first one, both the client and the music therapist played on djembes. The second one lasted nearly 14 minutes and, according to Simen, was particularly important because of his daring to play the piano for the first time and because of what emerged when the two played together. Simen said that he was afraid of improvising on the piano, but he still chose that instrument. The music therapist chose a drum kit. Musical intersubjectivity emerged during the improvisation.

The client introduced distinct notes in the high treble. Immediately, these notes resonated through increased intensity in the cymbals (absolute intensity). When the client made distinct clusters in the treble range, the music therapist matched the sound with the bass drum as a crossmodal way of responding. The client and the music therapist shared the beat, like a close musical wandering. Sometimes the steady beat changed through accelerando and diminuendo. At other times, both participants attuned to the temporal beat. There was a pattern of pulsation, unequally stressed between notes in the high treble and the structure in the percussion instrument (rhythm). This gradual change through time was grasped by the other and purposively continued by both client and therapist (duration). There was also an inner ebb and flow, an acceleration and increased intensity in the matching between the instruments (intensity contour). The joint sharing included this ebb and flow. The two people's attentiveness to each other silently increased as the music slowly faded away. A condensed awareness emerged. The client and the music therapist simultaneously glanced at each other within a microsecond of their pause, and both smiled. The client exhaled deeply and relaxed and then vocalized "Wow," followed by a "wow" from the therapist. The therapist's reflections on the session include the comment, "This is intersubjectivity in real life: The feeling of *I* know that *you* know that *I* know—and we both know. We've been very close to each other in the music today."

During the improvisation, the client held a very concentrated posture as he was leaning towards the piano. To him, this was the opposite of his normal behavior, in which his arms and legs seemed to move restlessly. Immediately after the improvisation, Simen (still sitting at the piano) indicated that he had not "tried to be clever," but simply attempted something he had not tried before:

> Cl: Sometimes I am afraid of trying all these new things.
> *Th: You can do it at your own pace, you know.*
> Cl: Yeah.
> *Th: Yeah—previously you didn't want to play the piano.*
> Cl: No (smiling and playing some notes on the piano), but so it happened.

During the verbal processing, Simen said, "I never did believe I would dare to try the piano ... but I did. ... Music describes feelings. At least it does to me. ... Music is about movement, rhythm, strength and intensity" (Trondalen, 2004a). Simen also realized that "music and feelings are connected. ... It is something to relate to when I am alone. Music and feeling—the music reflects my feelings." Through his exploration of the piano, Simen explored new possibilities of participation with an interesting outcome, such as not needing to vomit the half slice of bread he had eaten in the morning (Trondalen, 2011).

Simen acquired living memories of feeling—intersubjective sharing—connected to the music improvisation. He physically recognized the keys in touch with his fingers and felt the music through his sense, as he also related to the music therapist. His phenomenal, double-sensing body afforded him a lived experience to be transferred to his daily life. The different interaction formats of intersubjectivity were indeed put in play. The closing interview after one year of music therapy included the following exchange (Trondalen, 2004a):

> *Th: Is there anything you would like to bring with you from music therapy?*
> Cl: Yes, it has been fun. And I am bringing with me some concepts we have been exploring. I am aware of the link between the terms we have discussed in the verbal communication and what I have felt in the music.
> *Th: Here are two key words you have underlined in your summing up after each session. One is* clarity *and the other one is* regulation.

Cl: Yes, I was also thinking about those words.
Th: *What did you think about them?*
Cl: (Laughing) I thought I would like to include them in
my life.

The immediate joy of music making does not presuppose cognitive reflection, as the body is a carrier of subjectivity—the body self—while transcending the split between consciousness and the world, and between consciousness and the body. This client usually moved his arms and legs restlessly. In the present example, he adopted a concentrated posture while leaning toward the piano. I would suggest that the client's subjective perceiving body (corporeality and temporality) supported new relating experiences as opposed to the previous embodiment that had emerged from suffering an eating disorder.

Such a relating experience empowers the client's strengths, supports internal healing resources and nourish hope of a "normal" life; in other words, it supports life itself. Perhaps unconsciously, Simen wanted to try out a social practice (Bourdieu, 1998). This was an experience of participating in a socially normal relationship at both a personal and a relational level, while exploring "factors which unite to create the whole and complete form of beauty, which is the person" (Kenny, 1989, p. 75). Personal pleasure in music making and a sense of belonging are important elements for developing musical identity.

From a philosophical point of view, it seemed that the client was able to grasp meaning from the musical improvisation, as audibly expressed through a "Wow." The experience seemed to offer an immediate meaning without any explicit reflection upon it, a pre-linguistic being in the world (Holgersen, 2006). The client and the therapist talked about the music experience as well. Simen's body was relaxed and his voice was excited yet calm during the conversation. This musical sharing became important to him.

The next illustration of musical intersubjectivity comes from receptive music therapy. We have previously seen Ole, a man in his mid-fifties who attended five GIM sessions over a period of nine months. This example highlights his experience of dwelling in and surrendering to the music during his GIM experience in the here-and-now. In the verbal conversation before the music listening, Ole said that he was distressed. He listened to the GIM program *Peak Experience (Modified)*. The following interaction came shortly after his experience of "a taste of paradise" (described in chapter 8 above).

> During listening to *Fauré's Requiem* (In Paradisum), Ole said, "The music talks about entering into a greater freedom, greater life—ongoing growth." While listening to Wagner's *Lohengrin* (Prelude to Act I), he said, "Music is a different language—music speaks in another way—this music enlightens my mind—very long line—[*stay with the music*]—the music is building up and building up to this climax—*Now* I am grounded."

In the verbal conversation after the music listening experience, Ole stated that there are so many things in life that he cannot control, but that listening to this music gave him peace. "I was deeply touched by the music ... the music spoke so beautifully to me today," he said.

The music experience offered space and unconcealed some "rooms," thoughts and feelings that were "sleeping" in the client's busy daily life. Ole felt nurtured by the music itself. The client's lived experience seem to support another track of connecting to non-verbal and non-conscious experiences—an implicit knowing (Lyons-Ruth, 1998). The music experience obviously communicated meaning to the client during the listening, which came before he consciously reflected upon the lived experience. Recognition at an existential level supports a relational mode of surrender (Blom, 2014). I contend that Ole's existential dwelling in the music is musical intersubjectivity.

It seemed as if Ole consciously grasped his music experience, both while it happened and in the subsequent conversation. The connection between the immediate experiences of meaning supported and strengthened the verbal experience. The client drew attention to this relating experience in the music in his closing interview after completing GIM (Trondalen, 2016a). These inner experiences emerging in the music listening stayed with him outside the music therapy setting as well. For example, he spoke of them again when we randomly met on the street one year later. Indeed, there was a movement from dwelling in the presence of the other in a musical being to reflecting upon the experience and integrating it in his life. The experience supported the development of mentalization (Fonagy et al., 2002).

These music examples illustrate experiences of *expansion of the intersubjective field through music,* which is a potent experience in producing development and change (Tronick, 1998). Music therapy aims at an expansion of the client's lived experience and her or his intersubjective awareness through new relating experiences of music. Emotional availability and responsiveness through affect attunement and regulation are core elements in such a musical trail, as affect attunement is the mainstay of intersubjectivity (Stern, interviewed by Heje & Johansen, 1990). An expansion of self-experience, self-understanding, and joint meaning allows for change. A musical interaction aims at creating joint meaning in such a way that similarities and differences are explored and shared through music and musical elements, for example, through movements, rhythms, and dynamic shifts. The examples show the intersubjective field emerging through a musical improvisation and a music listening procedure in which the participants acquired the ability to experience the world and themselves through a relationship. Each individual became more, "bigger," and different from being on his own.

I think that Ansdell (2014, p. 159) expresses this dialogical stance in a fruitful way: "Being dialogical means never finalising a person, a relationship or a situation, but trying to keep things in play between us." Through keeping the dialogue going through and in music, an expanded experience of oneself and the other(s) offers new way of relating.

This new experience becomes a part of the client's (and the therapist's) lived story, her or his narrative. Such lived stories contribute to the activation of stored memories and the expectation of feelings, as in Stern's (1995) concept of RIGs (Representations of Interactions being Generalized). Experiences of interaction with others are stored very quickly and become a representation of generalized expectations of how to dialogue with each person we encounter. Important factors in this process are the feelings of contingency and agency. Contingency means that the individual experiences a connection in time between her or his initiative and the given response; agency relates to the person's sense of being able to influence her or his surroundings (Stern, 2000). These principles affect stored memories, which are rooted in expectations of how to relate with other people. Experiences of interactions with another person are stored and become building blocks for relational interplay, self-esteem, images, and ways of being with others.

An intersubjective perspective on relational music therapy offers a frame and dialogical exploration through a mutually influential dialogue based on musical elements. Through different and repeated senses of feelings in the interplay, these representations of memories of feelings (interaction being generalized) may be affected and updated (as RIGs). The new experience of being able to influence the musical interaction (self-agency) is compared to earlier stored memories of feelings. The comparison may result in an update and reassessment of earlier experiences. Hence, music therapy supports building blocks for ways of being with other people.

At a practical level, these renewed experiences of oneself with others may be recognized as expanded possibilities of participation and may contribute to a larger space for emotional differences, an increased sense of self, and intersubjective sharing. Again, this represents development and growth through expansion of the intersubjective field. It might be that such a broadening and expansion of meaning, in terms of understanding oneself and others more fully, can support a more sustainable life in a continuously changing world.

An intersubjective, relational experience through and in music is multilayered. Such an experience is measured in objective (chronos) time but is experienced within the subjective time frame (kairos). Within such an experience, both the musical theme and the process itself are important. The musical experience is represented as explicit and implicit knowledge. Examples of the explicit knowledge are the responses that the "music describes feelings" or that a particular piece of music gives "peace." The non-verbal and implicit level connects to *how to do things* with intimate others, like improvising or listening together in music therapy. This knowing is procedural. It is never reducible to techniques, but has to be attuned to in every new relational music experience.

Tronick (1998, p. 292) also recognized the importance of meetings of minds at different levels. Within such a meeting, the client and the therapist may experience what Tronick terms a "dyadic state of consciousness." A dyadically expanded state of consciousness is open to shared experiences and the development of new forms of participation. After a successful moment of meeting, the moving-along process (here, the music therapy process) resumes. However, it does so in a newly expanded musical intersubjective field that allows for a variety of new possibilities. These experiences change the musical relationship and reorganize the intersubjective field irreversibly, as the participants acquire the possibility to experience the world and themselves *through* a relationship.

For example, Simen's "wow" experience was neither verbalized nor interpreted during the music therapy process. I resonate with Stern (2004, p. 170), who said of another event, "It had worked its magic implicitly." This expansion of the intersubjective field gave Simen enough space and safety to comment on his fear later in the verbal processing: "I never did believe I would dare to try the piano ... but I did" (Trondalen, 2004a, p. 329). Such a comment, based on the recollection of a shared feeling voyage, can be a rich, emotional lived story (Stern, 2004).

With regard to the moving-along process and implicit changes, Stern (2004, p. 179) commented:

> Some consider this interaction as a sort of "micro-corrective emotional experience." I see it more as a new experience that does not repair the past by filling in a deficit, but rather creates a new experience that can be carried forward and built upon in the future.
>
> This view is not based on a deficit model, but one of creating contexts in which new emergent properties are permitted and encouraged to arise. These new emergent properties then establish the new context where something else can arise.

To me, this is an interesting statement, as nothing needs to be right or wrong in the music. The musical dialogue does not have deficits that needs to be repaired. Musical interaction is a source for interpersonal relating, and as such, it offers a new experience that can be carried forward, establishing a new basis for future development. The emergence of a new intersubjective field allows for an influential emotional experience through music. Older patterns of interaction are influenced by new experiences, which in turn create new ways of relating. Both the relationship and the relating experiences through music change the present while shedding light on the past within an anticipated future.

The previous examples illustrated intentionally shared mental states of being in the music. According to phenomenology, intentionality has two forms. One links to the pre-verbal being-in-the-world, in which one can perceive mentally and reach out with the body, without thinking about the movement of the hand (*Greifen*). The other form of intentionality is to seize (*Zeigen*), that is, to reflect upon the meaning of an item or an act (Holgersen, 2006). As human beings, we are always directed toward something, from which we create a variety of meanings in diverse modes and levels. The latter is exactly my point here; musical intersubjectivity shows its face in different ways. In Simen's story, the "wow" experience may be understood as a bodily being-in-the-world experience. In Ole's case, he commented on the (bodily) music listening experience, "The music spoke so beautifully to me today." For Ole, the experience permitted the uncovering of important things in his life that were previously not exposed.

The musical relationship in itself offers new ways of being with another, an existential experience different from anything else. Hence, one experiences the musical situation as a whole, acquiring self-agency as a first person as the experience itself is transformed into something new. In this way, musical intersubjectivity connects to the mode of surrender, and to the potential for transformation. Musical intersubjectivity offers an exploration and expansion of the intersubjective field, a way to develop and support new experiences in life.

Chapter 13

Power And Responsibility

Relationship is a real risk. The human being is existing within a relational matrix at different levels and in a variety of settings and contexts. As *homo communicans*, we are searching toward each other through different dimensions. Allowing oneself to become involved with another person is a risky sport. Skårderud (1998, p. 13) wrote:

> Strictly speaking, parachuting is not a terrible risk. It is merely copying life's real risks. Love, intimacy and *the others* are the real risks. What is river rafting to rejection? What is bungee-jumping to the loved one's call that never comes?

Uncertainty is always involved in dealing with the other. From a philosophical point of view, these life conditions are equally valid to the music therapist as to the client. Within a relational paradigm, we are all in the world together and therefore fellow travelers (Yalom, 2001). Bruscia (2014a, p. 145) also pointed out that interacting and playing with another person involves risk:

> Improvising is experimenting, and, as such, it is a trial and error undertaking that involves considerable risk. At every moment, something can go in an unwanted direction. ... The improviser is constantly confronted with the risk of failure and the limits of his capacity. In addition, there is always a risk of meaninglessness.

Musical interplay is not predictable and may or may not support a life-giving experience. I recall 12 year-old Silje's comments, "Music therapy is more difficult and more demanding than 'usual' therapy. ...

because you cannot hide within the music, and because you give more of yourself in the music making." Musical intersubjectivity is a potent space for development and change. It does, however, involve some paradoxical aspects.

For the music therapist, personal reflexivity is indeed important, as a relational music therapy comprises implications for the music therapist at a personal and professional level. Further, a therapeutic relationship always has an underlying dimension of power. The latter involves different layers related to personality, culture, and context in a broad sense. Therefore, about what, and about whose power, are we talking?

Philosophically, the client and therapist are subjects to each other. Mutual recognition and intersubjectivity abolish the need to mark independence and differences. To me, this consideration is indeed relevant within musical intersubjectivity, as music offers space to explore music as a multilayered experience. Talking about relating experiences through music, however, naturally involves the question of how mutual a therapeutic relationship can really be, since the therapist represents the authority in the relationship by virtue of her title and academic qualifications. One participant is most often seeking help and the other is defined as the helper; that relationship inevitably carries with it a difference in power (Skau, 1992). However, the client is a competent individual as well and one who contributes to the therapeutic relationship, perhaps even "helping" the therapist when the client finds the therapist is in need of support (Rolvsjord, 2014, 2015a, 2015b). An additional consideration is the power linked to electronic media. For example, a client can comment on or post a photo of a music therapist by name through Facebook, Twitter, Instagram, personal blogs, or similar media. The therapist, however, is bound by ethical obligations and cannot comment in the same way. Power is unequally distributed in connection to time and possibility.

A relational music therapy takes mutuality and equality into account. The musical relationship emerges within a relational field while supporting the participants' resources in an individual and social context. Within such a matrix, tension might arise—for example, between focusing on resources as experienced by the therapist and those experienced by the client. Similar tensions might arise with regard to the perception or performance of music. Music therapy strives at recognizing all musical expressions, regardless of the level or style of performance. The music therapist supports and recognizes the client's freedom to express her or his personal way of dealing with music in daily life and in music therapy. "In this way, music therapy may serve as one important counterpoint to elitist music culture" (Rolvsjord, 2010, p. 35).

Power has different faces and voices in therapy depending on what kind of position is placed in the foreground. For example, the emphasis could be on a feminist and postmodern position (empowerment) or an existential focus (authenticity) (Bruscia, 2014a). Interpreting the situation involves recognizing structures of power and freedom that one might or might not possess due to personal or social constraints. Power inevitably entails having power *over* something. It also relates to having the power to act through the individual's personal resources (Rolvsjord, 2010; Schwabe, 2005). It connects to empowerment (Rolvsjord, 2004) as both an individual and a social process (Zimmermann, 2000). It is a politically loaded term, as it includes power relations (Freire, 1970). Empowerment is a philosophy and a perspective. Therefore, one should be aware of the interaction between the various levels of empowerment (Hage & Lorentsen, 2005).

The authenticity of empowerment has many facets. As we have already noted, how mutual can a relationship really be when one is defined as therapist and the other as client? When does it become mutual? All clients have power over some of their health needs, which should be negotiated in the therapeutic relationship. Clients have free will and retain decisive responsibility for addressing their health needs that are in their power, but not for those that are outside their authority (Bruscia, 2014a). The therapist has the power to support and address some of the client's health needs, but not all of them. It is the same with the issue of motivation: the therapist may be able to motivate and perhaps influence the client to address her or his personal health needs, but the client, like the therapist, retains free will as a human being.

There is a mutual influence within a music therapy relationship. Social contexts and individual factors, including personal possibilities and constraints, psychically and mentally influence the possibilities of participation. Both the therapist and the client have their own free will, or power over themselves. However, as pointed out above, the therapist and the client bring different resources into the setting. "Briefly, it is inauthentic to assume that the therapist is helping a client when he is not, and it is also inauthentic to assume that the therapist is not helping a client when he is" (Bruscia 2014a, p. 294). The music therapist is responsible for acting in a way that is consistent with these powers and freedoms as well. One more aspect to contemplate is how the therapist's nature and condition contribute to what is shared and what is kept out of the music therapy process. Generalizing about power by equating the client and the music therapist with regard to power and freedom may lead to inauthenticity.

There are different levels and dimensions of power and power relationships in therapy, as both clients and therapist come with all shapes and forms of power. In music therapy, clients and music therapist often improvise together. Instruments (De Backer, 1999; Oldfield, Tomlinsen, & Loombe, 2015) also involve a potential distribution of power relationships (Hallsted & Rolvsjord, 2015; Trondalen, 2004a). Evaluating the balance of power is multilayered and complex. Power at its heart is about potentiality (Zur, 2015). Therefore, music belongs to everybody and can be linked to a human rights perspective (Krüger, 2012) At other times, the dimension of power is linked to gender and race (Hadley, 2013), music culture, values and cultural capital (Bordieu, 1998; Ruud, 1996, 2010), views of illness and pathology (Solli & Rolvsjord, 2015), and political, social, and ethical concerns (Aasgaard, 2002; Stige, 2002). Accordingly, music therapy and power relationships are also linked to discourses. Yet music therapy as a discourse is not free from or outside the bounds of language (Ansdell, 2003, 2014; Edwards, 2012). It is constructed in and through language as we negotiate identities and build relationships while searching for and finding moments of meaning at different levels.

Culture, personal qualities, and context in a broad sense influence the power structure of a relationship (Engedal, 1989; Stige, Malterud, & Midtgarden, 2009). There are varieties of music experiences within the different approaches in music therapy, and these are influenced by different power relationships as well. I would like to draw special attention to *experiences of spirituality* with its different facets. There seems to be a trend today toward recognizing spirituality in therapy more often than previously in public discussion and in research (Opsahl, 2012; Stålsett, 2012). During the last decades, a new field of discourse (Olsen, 2006) has emerged, resulting in a paradigm shift toward more reflection on human experience as an authentic source of divine revelation and vision.

In music therapy, both music making and listening to music afford spiritual experiences, although this facets seem to be most prominent within receptive music therapy, especially GIM. There are many different kinds of spiritual and transformative experiences. These experiences can be liberating, as they often affect basic human dignity at the deepest level (Trondalen, 2012). However, nobody lives in a vacuum. Clients also talk about spiritual experiences that do not lead to liberation. Repression of different and strange experiences through music may be motivated by a desire for control or power, or by inexperience. Spiritual experiences are powerful and can change people, (religious) practices, and society. They may consciously or unconsciously threaten those in power, to the extent that some people may call them demonic (Laugerud, 2012). This negatively oriented power exerted in response to spirituality denies positive experiences by leading to the opposite of liberation and connectedness; it reduces life quality radically and serves to split and confuse.

In music therapy, powerful spiritual experiences are linked to a universal phenomenon, as they are connected to a human being's deepest experiences and existential longings (Engedal, 2003). Human spirituality connects to longings for something life-giving, vitalizing, unifying, and integrative in life. It goes beyond the limited or controlled self and touches the human being's deepest value as a creation. These connections make us stronger and vulnerable at the same time.

The influence of negative power may be reduced by making structures of power transparent. Publishing stories about music therapy, with full awareness and informed consent, may reduce the privatization of experiences that therapeutic arrangements often represent (Isdahl & Skårderud, 1994).

Finally, it is important to consider our use of terms such as disease, health, or ill health. The use of music is usually presented as useful and in positive terms. There is a growing interest, however, in looking more closely at possible negative uses and effects of music, both in music therapy and in daily life (McFerran, Garrido, & Saarikallio, 2013; Saarikallio, Gold, & McFerran, 2015).

Chapter 14

Ethics

Working toward a noble ethical standard in music therapy is a constant process, systemically and personally. Yet I recognize that music therapy is always a part of a larger social system, which will necessarily affect our understanding of realities. This is, for example, visible in questions linked to society's concerns for "usefulness" and cost-effectiveness (Myrstad, 2001).

Music therapy offers an encounter with the *other* through music. Every relating experience through music is unique and multilayered, and it demands continuous reflection from a therapeutic point of view. Ethics and responsibility are indissolubly linked to each other, professionally and personally. All human experiences, resources, and constraints are to be met with humility and compassion. Writing about, experiencing, and participating in such an encounter is an ethical responsibility.

This book maintains the crucial influence of relationships. It advocates for relationships as the driving force for human development and growth, as we always live our lives in relation to others. The understanding of ethics also needs such a basis. The philosopher Lévinas offered one way of approaching ethics in a relating setting: the ethics of the *Other*. Bergo (2015, paragraph one) presented Lévinas' philosophy in this way:

> It is an interpretive, phenomenological description of the rise and repetition of the face-to-face encounter, or the intersubjective relation at its precognitive core; viz., being called by another and responding to that other. ... a continuum of sensibility and affectivity, in other words, sentience and emotion in their interconnection.

To *be seen* is reassuring, confirming, and crucial to every human being. Human sociality is expressed in the irreducible face-to-face relation that emerges from seeing the *Other* as the outstanding and irreplaceable creation that she or he is. According to Lévinas (1961/2012), this is the source of ethics. Lévinas developed his claims for the superiority of his ethics from the experience of the encounter with the *Other*.

Ethics in this sense does not emerge from a certain action or a specific moral code; it begins with face-to-face contact. Seeing and grasping the *Other's Face* leads to recognizing the person in her or his wholeness. Meaning derives from the relationship with the Other. It is within the face-to-face encounter (alterity, or "otherness") that I become what I am. We are approaching each other with a calling. This is a calling *to* us, one that demands a response. Through an encounter with the Other, I am made receptive, and at the same time, through the revelation of the face, I am called to responsibility. This response includes presence and care, an obligation of being *for* the Other. The Other makes me something that I am not able to become or experience on my own. "The Other precisely *reveals* himself in his alterity, not in a shock negating the I, but as the primordial phenomenon of gentleness," according to Lévinas (1961/2012, p. 150). The Other does not reveal herself or himself in a way that leads to reduction to sameness, as the Other is not knowable and cannot be made into an object of the self.

From a philosophical point of view, we can never expect the other to relate in a similar way as we do ourselves. Lévinas (1991, p. 84) stated, "I have always taken one more step towards him—which is possible only if this step is responsibility. In the responsibility which we have for one another, I have always one response more to give."

Transferring these concepts to music therapy, in the client's face, the therapist meets with a *vulnerability* not available for negotiation, and therefore it is not possible to be indifferent and unresponsive. Attention is attention to something because it is attention to someone (Lévinas, 1991). The meaning of therapy is therefore rooted in the meaning of a shared experience. As long as it is something that we can open up for and share with each other, such a shared life world offers new competencies for life.

From a theoretical point of view, the expansion of the intersubjective field supports new meaning and competencies. Within a joint and shared encounter, the physical presence of each person to the other through music offers meaning related to the capacities needed to exist and develop in the world. Practical examples could include the personal feeling of being recognized as I am through the creation of a song, an improvisation, or a joint receptive music listening experience, all of which promote increased self-esteem that leads to new possibilities of participation.

All the examples from actual music therapy sessions presented in this book are based on informed consent by the clients (Hammersley & Atkinson, 1996). The Norwegian Social Science Data Services and the Regional Committees for Medical and Health Research Ethics approved the examples stemming from research projects. The music therapy sessions were conducted in accordance with the Code of Ethics for music therapists (Dileo, 2000). Confidentiality is an important responsibility for the therapist: "The music therapist protects the confidentiality of the client at all times, including, verbal, written, audio and pictorial information regarding the client" (Maranto, 1993, p. 41). The client is to be protected and respected as an independent person with dignity. This respect includes how the client's experiences are represented in oral and written presentations. Such an ethical reflection is again a reminder of the professional dilemma that could arise between the music therapist's personal and professional need to perform research and developmental work and the client's need in a music therapy setting.

Epilogue

Semper Major

The human being is self-reflexive—a homo sapiens—and in fact the only species that reflects on its peculiar nature. Engedal (1996) suggested three basic perspectives when we are seeking to understand the process of creating a human identity.

First, the identity's dynamic basis is *the basic pattern of relating*. As human beings, we are all weaved together with other human beings, always seeking interpersonal communication and a response to our lives. The close relations in the first years of a human being's life are of vital importance. Experiences of recognition, predictability, coherence, trust and belonging in our first close relationships are indeed significant. These relationships are virtually pervaded by values, priorities, and interpretations related to social and cultural traditions. In music therapy, this relationship is formed by the client(s), the music, and the therapist, within a contextual framework.

The second perspective is *the basic pattern of life interpretation*. Such a foundation includes cultural traditions, knowledge of values, and ideology. Important issues in this perspective would include, for example, whether the community mediates its ideological view of life based on existential relevance to the human being. Does society value music as a meaningful way to support life interpretation, and does it approve music as a beneficial part of identity development for all people? Is music ideologically relevant as a contributor to the feeling of connectedness in society? These questions can be particularly significant for youngsters as they seek to develop a trustworthy and integrated interpretation of self. Music therapy offers music, images through music listening, and verbal conversations, all of which may support a useful life interpretation and development of one's personal identity within society.

The third perspective, *the basic pattern of existential being*, is linked to generative enforcement. This pattern includes (a) the intimacy of a personal relationship, (b) being productive in society, and (c) the life form of cultural creativity. Accordingly, existence connects to personal sexuality (*generativity*), education, and social belonging, and to how we express ourselves through our creativity (*life meaning*). Music therapy, particularly relational music experiences, support a web of relevance and meaning to the (existential) life world of the client.

Standing up for oneself (autonomy) is often a core theme in music therapy. At the same time, as human beings we are relationally bound to each other. This position creates a tension of existential dimensions, autonomy versus relation. I would suggest that a relational music experience offers a welcome, inviting an individual to surrender to and dwell in a musical presence, alone yet connected; it is a gift infected with hope. I propose that all these perspectives are basic to understanding the process of forming our identity, or who we are as human beings. Identity is not a fixed item, but an ongoing process. We are constantly being remade anew during a life span, and relational music experiences can be one of those remakers (Bonde et al., 2013; Ruud, 1997/2013). Relational experiences through music frame and support our ongoing creative processes, activities invested with that vital quality of hope (Aldridge, 1996).

Music is ambiguous and allows for experiences and interpretations on many levels. Clients and music therapists can feel revitalized through relating and connecting experiences that derive from music. In the music, the client and the therapist move along together, as they perform their musical lives within the tension that accompanies being alone (autonomy) at the same time as they are together (in relation). It is within this tension that the human being is challenged to develop a sustainable yet sufficiently flexible identity.

In music therapy and in life in general, I am constanly reminded that all human beings are always more than—*semper major*—what meets the eye. What we perform in life—musically, biologically, socially, or spiritually—does not disclose the depths in our existence.

References

Aasgaard, T. (2002). *Song Creations by Children with Cancer: Process and Meaning* (Unpublished doctoral dissertation). Aalborg University, Aalborg, Denmark.

Abrams, B. (2002). Definitions of Transpersonal BMGIM Experience. *Nordic Journal of Music Therapy, 11*(2), 103–126.

Aigen, K. S. (2014). *The Study of Music Therapy: Current Issues and Concepts.* New York and London: Routledge.

Aldridge, D. (1991, March). Aesthetics and the Individual in the Practice of Medical Research. *Journal of the Royal Society of Medicine, 84,* 147–150.

Aldridge, D. (1996). *Music Therapy Research and Practice in Medicine: From Out of the Silence.* London: Jessica Kingsley Publishers.

Aldridge, D. (2000). *Spirituality, Healing and Medicine.* London: Jessica Kingsley Publishers.

Alvesson, M., & Sköldberg, K. (1994). *Tolkning och reflektion. Vetenskapsfilosofi och kvalitativ metod.* Lund: Studentlitteratur.

Alvin, J. (1966/1975). *Music Therapy.* London: John Clare Books.

Ansdell, G. (2003). The Stories We Tell. Some Meta-theoretical Reflections on Music Therapy. *Nordic Journal of Music Therapy, 12*(2), 152–159.

Ansdell, G. (2014). *Where Music Helps in Music Therapy and Everyday Life.* Farnham and Brulington: Ashgate.

Ansdell, G., Davidson, J., Magee, W., Meehan, J., & Procter, S. (2010). From "This ****ing Life" to "That's Better" … in Four Minutes: An Interdisciplinary Study of Music Therapy's "Present Moments" and their Potential for Affect Modulation. *Nordic Journal of Music Therapy, 19*(1), 3–28.

Ansdell, G., & DeNora, T. (2016). *Musical Pathways in Recovery: Community Music Therapy & Mental Wellbeing.* London: Routledge.

Austad, A. (1996). Ansikt til ansikt. Tanker om relasjon og nøytralitet i psykoterapi. *Tidsskrift for sjelesorg, 1,* 30–37.

Austin, D. (1999). Vocal Improvisation in Analytically Oriented Music Therapy with Adults. In T. Wigram & J. De Backer (Eds.), *Clincial*

Applications of Music Therapy in Psychiatry (pp. 141-157). London: Jessica Kingsley Publishers.

Austin, D. (2006). Songs of Self: Vocal Psychotherapy for Adults Traumatized as Children. In L. Carey (Ed.), *Expressive and Creative Arts Methods for Trauma Survivors* (pp. 133-152). London: Jessica Kingsley Publishers.

Axelsen, E. D., & Hartmann, E. (Eds.). (1999). *Veier til forandring. Virksomme faktorer i psykoterapi.* Oslo: Cappelen Akademiske Forlag A/S.

Baker, F. A. (2015). *Therapeutic Songwriting.* New York: Palgrave Macmillan.

Baker, F., & Wigram, T. (Eds.). (2004). *Songwriting: Methods, Techniques and Clinical Applications for Music Therapy Clinicians, Educators and Students.* London: Jessica Kingsley Publishers.

Bateson, G. (1973). *Steps to an Ecology of Mind.* London; Paladin, Granada

Bateson, M. C. (1975). Mother-infant Exchanges: The Epigenesis of Conversational Interaction. *Annals of the New York Academy of Sciences, 263,* 101–113.

Bauer, J. (2007). *Varför jag känner som du känner. Intuitiv kommunikasjon och hemligheten med spegelneuronen.* Stockholm: Natur och Kultur.

Beck, B. D. (2012). *Guided Imagery and Music (GIM) with Adults on Sick Leave Suffering from Work-related Stress: A mixed Methods Experimental Study* (Unpublished doctoral dissertation). Aalborg University, Aalborg, Denmark.

Beebe, B., Knoblauch, S., Rustin, J., & Sorter, D. (2005). An Expanded View of Forms of Intersubjectivity in Infancy and Their Application to Psychoanalysis. In B. Beebe, S. Knoblauch, J. Rustin & D. Sorter (Eds.), *Forms of Intersubjectivity in Infant Research and Adult Treatment* (pp. 55-88) . New York: Other Press

Benestad, F. (1976). *Musikk og tanke. Hovedretninger i musikkestetikkens historie fra antikken til vår egen tid.* Oslo: Aschehoug.

Bengtsson, I. (1973/1977). *Musikvetenskap. En översikt.* Stockholm, Göteborg, and Lund: Scandinavian University Books.

Benjamin, J. (1990). An Outline of Intersubjectivity: The Development of Recognition. *Psychonalytic Psychology, 7 (Suppl.)*, 33–43.

Benjamin, J. (2004). Beyone Doer and Done to: An intersubjective view of thirdness. *Psychoanalytic Quarterly, New York, LXXIII*, 5–46.

Bergo, B. (2015, Summer). "Emmanuel Lévinas". In E. N. Zalta (Ed.), *The Stanford Encyclopedia of Philosophy.* Retrieved July, 24, 2014 from http://plato.stanford.edu/archives/sum2015/entries/levinas/

Bernth, I. (1995/1997). Innledning (B. Nake, Trans.). In L. Havnesköld & P. R. Mothander (Eds.), *Utviklingspsykologi. Psykodynamisk teori i et nytt perspektiv* (pp. 9-18). København: Hans Reitzels Forlag A/S.

Binder, P. E., Nielsen, G. H., Vøllestad, J., Holgersen, H., & Schanche, E. (2006). Hva er relasjonell psykoanalyse? Nye psykoanalytiske perspektiver på samhandling, det ubevisste og selvet. *Tidsskrift for Norsk Psykologforening, 43*(9), 899–908.

Bjørkvold, J.-R. (1989). *Det musiske menneske.* Oslo: Freidig Forlag.

Blom, K. M. (2014). Experiences of Transcendence and the Process of Surrender in Guided Imagery and Music (GIM): Development of New Understanding through Theories of Intersubjectivity and Change in Psychotherapy (Unpublished doctoral dissertation). Aalborg University, Denmark.

Blom, K. M., & Wrangsjö, B. (2013). *Intersubjektivitet: Det mellanmänskliga i vård och vardag.* Lund: Studentlitteratur.

Blood, A. J., Zatorre, R. J., Bermundez, P., & Evans, A. C. (1999). Emotional Responses to Pleasant and Unpleasant Music Correlate with Activity in Paralimbic Brain Regions. *Nature Neuroscience*(2), 382-387.

Bonde, L. O. (2000). Metaphor and Narrative in Guided Imagery and Music. *Journal of the Association for Music and Imagery, 7*, 59–76.

Bonde, L. O. (2009). *Musik og menneske: Introduktion til musikpsykologi.* Frederiksberg C: Samfundslitteratur.

Bonde, L. O. (2011). Health Musicing: Music Therapy or Music and Health? A Model, Empirical Examples and Personal Reflections. *Music & Arts in Action, 2*(2), 120–135.

Bonde, L. O. (Ed.). (2014). *Musikterapi: Teori, uddannelse, praksis, forskning.* Aarhus: KLIM.

Bonde, L. O. (2015). The Current State of Music Therapy Theory? *Nordic Journal of Music Therapy, 24*(2), 167–175. doi: http://dx.doi.org/10.1080/08098131.2014.987805

Bonde, L. O., Skånland, M. S., Ruud, E., & Trondalen, G. (Eds.). (2013). *Musical Life Stories. Narratives on Health Musicking.* Oslo: NMH-publikasjoner 2013:5, Skriftserie fra Senter for musikk og helse, Oslo: Norwegian Academy of Music. (vol. 5).

Bonny, H. L. (1976). *Music and Psychotherapy: A Handbook and Guide Accompanied by Eight Music Tapes to be Used by Practitioners of Guided Imagery and Music.* (Unpublished doctoral dissertation). Union Graduate School of the Union of Experimenting Colleges and Universities, Baltimore, MD, USA.

Bonny, H. L. (1978). *The Role of Taped Music Programs in the GIM Process: Theory and Product.* GIM Monograph #2. Baltimore, MD: ICM Books.

Bonny, H. (2002). *Music & Consciousness: The Evolution of Guided Imagery and Music.* Gilsum: Barcelona Publishers.

Bourdieu, P. (1998). *Practical Reason: On the Theory of Action.* Stanford, CA: Stanford University Press.

Bordin, E. S. (1979). The Generalizability of the Psychoanalytic Concept of the Working Alliance. *Psychotherapy: Theory, Research & Practice, 16*(3), 252–260. doi: http://dx.doi.org/10.1037/h0085885

Boston Change Process Study Group (2010). *Change in Psychotherapy: A Unifying Paradigm.* New York and London: W. W. Norton & Company

Bowlby, J. (1988). *A Secure Base.* London: Routledge.

Bradt, J., Dileo, C., & Portvin, N. (2013). Music for Stress and Anxiety Reduction in Coronary Heart Disease Patients. *Cochrane Database of Systematic Reviews, Dec 28*(12:CD006577). doi: 10.1002/14651858.CD006577.pub

Bradt, J., & Dileo, C. (2014). Music Interventions For Mechanically Ventilated Patients. *Cochrane Database of Systematic Review, Dec 9*(12:CD006902). doi: 10.1002/14651858.CD006902.pub3

Brantzæg, I., Smith, L., & Torsteinson, S. (2011). *Mikroseparasjoner. Tilknytning og behandling*. Bergen: Fagbokforlaget.

Bråten, S. (1998). *Intersubjective Communication and Emotion in Early Ontogeny*: Cambridge University Press.

Bråten, S. (2007). *Dialogens speil i barnet og språkets utvikling*. Oslo: Abstrakt forlag.

Brautaset, H., Egebjerg, I., & Johns, U. T. (2012). Terapeututvikling. Utvikling av sensitivitet og oppmerksomt nærvær i det terapeutiske møtet. In B. Svendsen, U. T. Johns, H. Brautaset, & I. Egebjerg (Eds.), *Utviklingsrettet intersubjektiv psykoterapi med barn og unge* (pp. 229–253). Bergen: Fagbokforlaget.

Bruner, J. (1975). From Communication to Language: A Psychological Perspective. *Cognition, 3*, 322–387.

Bruscia, K. E. (1987). *Improvisational Models of Music Therapy*. Springfield, IL: Charles C. Thomas.

Bruscia, K. E. (1998). *Defining Music Therapy* (2nd ed.). Lower Village: Barcelona Publishers.

Bruscia, K. E. (2014a). *Defining Music Therapy* (3rd ed.). University Park, IL: Barcelona Publishers.

Bruscia, K. E. (2014b). Discography of Guided Imagery and Music (GIM) Programs. Gilsum, NH: Barcelona Publishers.

Bruscia, K. E., & Grocke, D. E. (Eds.). (2002). *Guided Imagery and Music: The Bonny Method and Beyond*. Gilsum, NH: Barcelona Publishers.

Buber, M. (1970). *I and Thou* (W. Kaufmann, Trans.). New York: Charles Schribner's Son.

Buller, J. (2002). What Is It Like to Be an Injured Musician? *Canadian Music Educator, 43*(4), 20–23.

Bunt, L., & Stige, B. (2014). *Music Therapy. An Art Beyond Words* (2nd ed.). London and New York: Routledge.

Børstad, M. (1992). Intersubjektivitet i lys av dialektisk relasjonsteori. In E. Bae & J. E. Waastad (Eds.), *Erkjennelse og anerkjennelse, perspektiv på relasjoner* (pp. 114–142). Oslo: Universitetsforlaget.

Christensen, E. (2012). *Music Listening, Music Therapy, Phenomenology and Neuroscience* (Unpublished doctoral dissertation). Aalborg University, Aalborg, Denmark.

Clark, M. F. (1995). The Therapeutic Implications of The Hero's Myth in GIM Therapy. *Journal of the Association for Music and Imagery, 4*, 49–65.

Clark, M. (2002). Music Programs for Guided Imagery and Music (GIM). In K. E. Bruscia & D. E. Groscke (Eds.), *Guided Imagery and Music: The Bonny Method and Beyond* (Appendix F). Gilsum, NH: Barcelona Publishers.

Cushman, P. (1991). Ideology Obscured: Political Uses of the Self in Daniel Stern's Infant. *American Psychologist, 46*, 201–219.

Damasio, A. (2000). *The Feeling of What Happens: Body, Emotions and the Making of Consciousness.* London: Vintage.

Davis, M., & Wallbridge, D. (1981/2011). Boundary and Space: An Introduction to the Work of D. W. Winnicott. New York: Brunner/Mazel Publishers; London: H. Karnac (Books) Ltd.

De Backer, J. (1999). Specific Aspects of The Music Therapy Relationship to Psychiatry. In T. Wigram & J. De Backer (Eds.), *Clinical Applications of Music Therapy in Psychiatry.* London and Philadelphia: Jessica Kingsley Publishers.

de Labbé, M. B. (2010). *Slagen från ditt hjärta är rytmen av din själ.* (Unpublished master thesis), Norwegian Academy of Music, Oslo, Norway

Decker-Voigt, H.-H. (2012). *Zwischen Tönen und Worten; Ein Reader mit Aufsätzen, Reden und Interviews Reihe zeitpunkt musik.* Wiesbaden: Dr. Ludwig Reichert Verlag.

DeNora, T. (2000). *Music in Everyday Life.* Cambridge: Cambridge University Press.

DeNora, T. (2013). *Music Asylums: Wellbeing Through Music in Everyday Life.* Farmham and Burlington: Ashgate.

Dileo, C. (2000). *Ethical Thinking in Music Therapy.* Cherry Hill, NJ: Jeffrey Books.

Dileo, C. (Ed.). (2015). *Advanced Practice in Medical Music Therapy: Case Reports.* Cherry Hill, NJ: Jeffrey Books.

Dileo, C., & Loewy, J. V. (Eds.). (2005). *Music Therapy at the End of Life.* Cherry Hill, NJ: Jeffrey Books.

Duesund, L., & Skårderud, F. (2003). Use the Body, and Forget the Body: Treating Anorexia Nervosa with Adapted Physical Activity. *Clinical Child Psychology and Psychiatry, 8*(1), 53–72.

Eckhoff, R. (1997a). *Kroppsselv og interkroppslighet i musikkterapi. Konsekvenser for anoreksibehandling - teori og erfaringer.* (Unpublished master thesis), University of Oslo, Oslo, Norway

Eckhoff, R. (1997b). Musikk og kropp. Filosofisk grunnlag og metodisk anvendelse i musikkterapi med psykiatriske pasienter. *Musikkterapi, 22*(4), 17-39.

Edwards, J. (2012). We Need to Talk About Epistemology: Orientations, Meaning, and Interpretation within Music Therapy Research. *Journal of Music Therapy, 49*(4), 372-394.

Eide, H., & Eide, T. (1996). *Kommunikasjon i relasjoner.* Oslo: Ad Notam Gyldendal AS.

Elefant, C. (2002). *Enhancing Communication in Girls with Rett Syndrome through Songs in Music Therapy* (Unpublished doctoral dissertation). Aalborg University, Aalborg, Denmark.

Emde, R. (1990). Mobilizing Fundamental Modes of Developing: Emphatic Availability and Therapeutic Action. *Journal of American Psychoanalytic Association, 38*(4), 881-913.

Emde, R. N., & Sorce, J. E. (1983). The Rewards of Infancy: Emotional Availability and Maternal Referencing. In J. D. Call, E. Galenson, & R. Tyson (Eds.), *Frontiers of Infant Psychiatry* (Vol. 2, pp. 17-30). New York: Basic Books.

Engedal, L. G. (1989). Ecce homo. Refleksjoner omkring sammenhengen mellom menneskebilde og psykoterapeutisk teoridannelse. *Nordisk Psykologi, 41*(4), 284-300. doi: 10.1080/00291463.1989.10636982

Engedal, L. G. (1996). Den andres ansikt. Refleksjoner om sammenhengen mellom kristen tro og personlig identitet. *Prismet, Pedagogisk Tidsskrift, 3,* 114-122.

Engedal, L. G. (2003). Spiritualitet og teologi. *Ung teologi, 2,* 47-56.

Eriksson, A. K. (2001). Grundpuls i musikterapeutiske processer. Fenomenet grundpuls och desss betydelse i musikkterapeutiska processer belyst ur Nordoff och Robbins modell samt modern utvecklingspsykologi. *Musikkterapi, 26*(2), 5-25.

Eschen, J. T. (Ed.) (2002). *Analytical Music Therapy.* London and Philadelphia: Jessica Kingsley Publishers.

Fagius, J. (2001). *Hemisfärernas musik. Om musikhändtering i hjärnan.* Göteborg: Bo Ejeby förlag.

Fagius, J., & Lagercrantz, H. (2007). Barnet, hjärnan, musiken och sången. In G. Fagius (Ed.), *Barn och sång: Om rösten, sångerna och vägen dit* (pp. 32-41). Lund: Studentlitteratur.

Farber, B. A., & Lane, J. S. (2001). Positive Regard. *Psychotherapy: Theory, Research, Practice, Training, 38*(4), 390-395. doi: http://dx.doi.org/10.1037/0033-3204.38.4.390

Ferrara, L. (1984). Phenomenology as a Tool for Musical Analysis. *Musical Quarterly, 70*(3), 355-373.

Ferrara, L. (2005). Philosophical Inquiry: Concepts and Tecniques. In R. P. Phelps, R. H. Sadoff, , E. C. Warburton, & L. Ferrara (Eds.), *A Guide to Research in Music Education* (5th ed.), (Chapter 4). Lanham, MD: Scarecrow Press.

Figley, C. R. (2002). Compassion Fatigue: Psychotherapists' Chronic Lack of Self Care. *Psychotherapy in Practice, 58*(11), 1433-1441. doi: 10.1002/jclp.10090

Fjermestad, K. W. (2011). Terapeutisk allianse i kognitiv atferdsterapi med barn og ungdom. *Tidsskrift for Norsk Psykologforening, 48,* 12-15.

Fonagy, P., & Bateman, A. (2006). Mechanism of Change in Mentalization-Based Treatment of Borderline Personality Disorder. *Journal of Clinical Psychology, 62,* 411-430.

Fonagy, P., Gergely, G., Jurist, E. L., & Target, M. (2002). *Affect Regulation, Mentalization, and the Development of the Self.* New York: Other Press.

Fonagy, P., & Target, M. (1997). Attachment and Reflective Function: Their Role in Self-Organization. *Development and Psychopathology, 9,* 679-700.

Fonagy, P., & Target, M. (1998). Mentalization and the Changing Aims of Child Psychoanalysis. *Psychoanalytic Dialogues, 8,* 87-114.

Forinash, M. (Ed.). (2001). *Music Therapy Supervision.* Gilsum, NH: Barcelona Publishers.

Freire, P. (1970). *Pedagogy of the Oppressed.* New York: Continuum.

Freud, S. (1920). *Beyond the Pleasure Principle.* London: Hogarth Press.

Frohne-Hagemann, I. (1998). The "Musical Life Panorama": A Facilitating Method in the Field of Clinical and Sociocultural

Music Therapy. *Nordisk Tidsskrift for Musikkterapi*, 7(2), 104–112.

Frohne-Hagemann, I. (2015). A Mentalization-Based Approach to Guided Imagery and Music. In D. Grocke & T. Moe (Eds.), *Guided Imagery & Music (GIM) and Music Imagery Methods for Individual and Group Therapy* (pp. 169–178). London and Philadelphia: Jessica Kingsley Publishers.

Gabrielson, A. (2011). *Strong Experiences with Music: Music is Much More than just Music*. Oxford: Oxford University Press.

Garred, R. (1996). Musikkterapeutisk improvisasjon som "møte". *Nordisk Tidsskrift for Musikkterapi*, 5(2), 76–86.

Garred, R. (2001). The Ontology of Music in Music Therapy. *Voices. A World Forum for Music Therapy*, 1(3). doi: 10.15845/voices.v1i3.63

Garred, R. (2006). *Music as Therapy: A Dialogical Perspective*. Gilsum, NH: Barcelona Publishers.

Gerbert, F. (2010). Wenn Arbeit krank macht. Burn-out: das Leiden einer modernen Gesellschaft. Warum die Zahl der Ausgebrannten wächst. *Focus*, 10(10), 92–103.

Glomb, S. (2007). Berufsspezifische Belastungen und Burnout bei Musiktherapeutinnen. *Musiktherapeutische Umschau*, 28(4), 365–369.

Goldberg, F. S. (2002). A Holographic Field Theory Model of The Bonny Method of Guided Imagery and Music (BMGIM). In K. E. Bruscia & D. E. Grocke (Eds.), *Guided Imagery and Music. The Bonny Method and Beyond* (pp. 359-378). Gilsum, NH: Barcelona Publishers.

Gouck, P. (Ed.). (2000). *Musical Healing in Cultural Contexts*. Aldershot: Ashgate.

Grimen, H. (2009). *Hva er tillit?* Oslo: Universitetsforlaget.

Grocke, D. E. (1999). *A Phenomenological Study of Pivotal Moments in Guided Imagery and Music Therapy* (Unpublished doctoral dissertation). University of Melbourne, Victoria, Australia.

Grocke, D. (2002a). The Bonny Music Programs. In D. Grocke & K. E. Bruscia (Eds.), *Guided Imagery and Music. The Bonny Method and Beyond* (pp. 99–136). Lower Village: Barcelona Publishers.

Hadley, S. (2013). *Experiencing Race as a Music Therapist: Personal Narratives*. Gilsum, NH: Barecelona Publishers.

Hage, A. M., & Lorensen, M. (2005). A Philosophical Analysis of the Concept of Empowerment; The Fundament of an Education-programme to the Frail Elderly. *Nursing Philosophy, 6*, 235-246.

Hallsted, J., & Rolvsjord, R. (2015). The Gendering of Musical Instruments: What is That? Why Does it Matter to Music Therapy? *Nordic Journal of Music Therapy*. Published online 23 Sept 2015, doi: 10.1080/08098131.2015.1088057

Hammersley, M., & Atkinson, P. (1996). *Feltmetodikk. Grunnlaget for feltarbeid og feltforskning*. Oslo: Ad Notam Gyldendal.

Hannibal, N. (2000). *Præverbal Overføring i Musikterapi: kvalitativ undersøgelse af overføringsprocesser i den musikalske interaktion* (Unpublished doctoral dissertation). Aalborg University, Aalborg, Denmark.

Hannibal, N. (2013). Mentaliseringsbaseret behandling og musikterapi. *Musikterapi i psykiatrien online (MIPO), 8*(1), 4-16.

Hannibal, N. (2014a). Implicit and Explicit Mentalization in Music Therapy in Psychiatric Treatment of People with Borderline Personality Disorder. In J. De Backer & J. Sutton (Eds.), *The Music in Music Therapy—Psychodynamic Music Therapy in Europe: Clinical, Theoretical and Research Approaches* (pp. 213-225). London: Jessica Kingsley Publishers.

Hannibal, N. (2014b). Mentaliseringsbasert terapi. In L. O. Bonde (Ed.), *Musikterapi: Teori, uddannelse, praksis, forskning* (pp. 119-122). Aarhus: KLIM.

Hannibal, N., Pedersen, I. N., Bonde, L. O., Bertelsen, L., Lund, H., & Dammeyer, C. (2013). Manual for procesorientert musikterapi med personer med personlighedsforstyrrelser. *Musikterapi i Psykiatrien Online (MIPO), 2*, 64-80.

Hansen, B. R. (1991a). Betydningen av oppmerksomhet og samspill i psykoterapi med barn. *Tidsskrift for Norsk Psykologforening, 28*, 779-788.

Hansen, B. R. (1991b). *Den første dialogen: En studie av spedbarnets oppmerksomhet i samspill*. Oslo: Solum Forlag.

Hansen, B. R. (1996). Den affektive dialogen i psykoterapi med barn. Implikasjoner fra nyere spedbarnsforskning. In M. Kjær (Ed.),

Skjønner du? Kommunikasjon med barn (pp. 79-96). Oslo: Kommuneforlaget.

Hansen, B. R. (2010). Affektive dialoger. Fra regulering til mentalisering. In V. Moe, K. Slinning & M. Bergum (Eds.), *Håndbok i sped-og småbarns psykiske helse* (pp. 116–136). Oslo: Gyldendal Norsk Forlag.

Hansen, B. R. (2012). *I dialog med barnet. Intersubjektivitet i utvikling og psykoterapi*. Oslo: Gyldendal Norsk Forlag A/S.

Hanser, S. B., & Mandel, S. E. (2010). *Manage Your Stress and Pain Through Music*. Boston: Berklee Press.

Haugsgjerd, S., Jensen, P., & Karlsson, B. (1998). *Perspektiver på psykisk helse. En innføring for helse- og sosialfagene*. Oslo: Ad Notam Gyldendal.

Haugvik, M., & Johns, U. (2008). Facets of Structure and Adaption: A Qualitative Study of Time-limited Psychotherapy with Children Experiencing Difficult Family Situations. *Clinical Child Psychology and Psychiatry, 13*(2), 235-252. doi: http://ccp.sagepub.com/cgi/content/abstract/13/2/235

Havnesköld, L., & Mothander, P. R. (1995/1997). *Utviklingspsykologi. Psykodynamisk teori i et nytt perspektiv* (B. Nake, Trans.). Copenhagen: Hans Reitzels Forlag A/S.

Hegi, F. (2015). Improvisation, Bildung und Therapie. *Musiktherapeutische Umschau, 36*(2), 119-127.

Heje, T., & Johansen, H. (1990). Nye strømninger i barnepsykologien: Daniel N. Stern— En presentasjon og et intervju. *Impuls, 3*, 38–44.

Hellsten, T. (2011). Jo mindre du gjør, dess mer får du gjort. *Strek, 4*, 34–41.

Henser, C., McFerran, K. S., Killacky, E., & McGorry, P. (2015, December). How Can Research Practice Promote Young People's Recovery from Mental Illness? A Critical Look at the Australian Context. *Youth Voice Journal, December 2015- Online.* Http://youthvoicejournal.com/

Hills, B., Norman, I., & Forster, L. (2000). A Study of Burnout and Multidiciplinary Team-Working amongst Professional Music Therapists. *British Journal of Music Therapy, 14*(1), 32–40.

Honneth, A. (1995). *The Struggle for Recognition. The Moral Grammer of Social Conflicts* (J. Anderson, Trans.). Cambridge: The MIT Press.

Holck, U. (2004). Turn-Taking in Music Therapy with Children with Communication Disorders. *British Journal of Music Therapy, 18*(2), 45–54.

Holgersen, S.-E. (2006). Den kropslige vending. En fænomenologisk undersøgelse af musikalsk intersubjektivitet. In F. V. Nielsen & S. G. Nielsen (Eds.), *Nordisk musikkpedagogisk årbok* (pp. 33–57). Oslo: Norges musikkhøgskole. (vol. 8).

Horgen, P. (Ed.). (2000). *Music as Medicine. The History of Music Therapy since Antiquity.* Aldershot, Burlington, VT, Singapore and, Sidney: Ashgate.

Hougaard, E. (1996). *Psykoterapi. Teori og forskning.* Copenhagen: Dansk Psykologisk Forlag.

Husserl, E. (1964). *The Phenomenology of Internal Time-Consciousness* (J.S. Churchill, Trans.) Bloomington: Indiana University Press.

Husserl, E. (1999). *The Idea of Phenomenology. Edmund Husserl Collected Works vol. VIII.* (L. Hardy, Trans.). Dortrecht, Boston, London: Kluwer Academic Publishers.

Ihlen, B.-M., & Ihlen, H. (2003). *På seg selv kjenner man ingen andre. Om kommunikasjon og teambygging.* Oslo: Cappelen.

Isdahl, P. J., & Skårderud, F. (1994). Uttrykksterapi. In F. Skårderud (Ed.), *Nervøse spiseforstyrrelser* (pp. 293-299). Oslo: Universitetsforlaget.

Jampel, P. F. (2011). Performance in Music Therapy: Experiences in five dimension. *Voices. A World Forum for Music Therapy, 11*(1). https://voices.no/index.php/ voices/article/view/275/440

Johansson, K. (2009). Uten kropp, ingen musikk: om kroppsfilosofi og kroppens rolle i musikkterapi. *Musikkterapi, 3,* 6-17.

Johns, U. (1993). Intersubjektivitet som grunnlag for utvikling. *Spesialpedagogikk*(3), 41–46.

Johns, U. (1994). Når musikken møtes ... Betraktninger med utgangspunkt i Björn Wrangsjös foredrag. *Nordisk Tidsskrift for Musikkterapi, 3*(2), 84–85.

Johns, U. T. (2008). "Å bruke tiden—hva betyr det egentlig": Tid og relasjon - et intersubjektivt perspektiv. In G. Trondalen & E. Ruud (Eds.), *Perspektiver på musikk og helse. 30 år med norsk musikkterapi,* (pp. 67–84). Oslo: NMH-publikasjoner 2008:3, Skriftserie fra Senter for musikk og helse, (vol. 1).

Johns, U. T. (2012). Vitalitetsformer i musikk. In G. Trondalen & K. Stensæth (Eds.), *Barn, musikk, helse* (pp. 29-44). Oslo: NMH-publikasjoner 2012:3. Skriftserie fra Senter for musikk og helse, (vol. 3).

Johns, U. T., & Svendsen, B. (2012). Utviklingsrettet intersubjektiv terapi med barn. In B. Svendsen, U. T. Johns, H. Brautaset & I. Egebjerg (Eds.), *Utviklingsrettet intersubjektiv psykoterapi med barn og unge* (pp. 35-73). Bergen: Fagbokforlaget.

Johns, U. T., & Svendsen, B. (2016). *Håndbok i tidsavgrenset intersubjektiv terapi for barn (TIB). Kunnskapgrunnlag, behandlingsprinsipper og eksempler.* Bergen: Fagbokforlaget.

Johnsen, A., Sundet, R., & Thorsteinsson, V. W. (2000). Daniel Sterns selvutviklingsmodell. In A. Johnsen, R. Sundet, & V. W. Thorsteinsson (Eds.), *Samspill og selvutvikling: nye veier i relasjonsorienterte terapier* (pp. 19-54). Oslo: Universitetsforlaget.

Kallevik, S. A. (2007). Øyeblikkets betydning i mesterlig mestermøte. *Tidsskrift for Norsk Psykologforening, 44*(10), 1261-1263.

Karterud, S., & Monsen, J. T. (Eds.). (1997). *Selvpsykologi. Utviklingen etter Kohut.* Oslo: Ad Notam Gyldendal.

Kenny, C. B. (1989). *The Field of Play.* Atascadero, CA: Ridgeview Publishing.

Kenny, C. (2002). Are we Really Looking for an "Ontology"? Response to Rudy Garred's Essay in Voices. *Voices. A World Forum for Music Therapy, July 15.* https://voices.no/community/?q=content/ dialogue-about-music-therapy-theory

Killingmo, B. (1999). Den åpnende samtalen. *Tidsskrift for den norske lægeforening, 119*(1), 56-59.

Kim, J. (2014). The Trauma of Parting: Endings of Music Therapy with Children with Autism Spectrum Disorders. *Nordic Journal of Music Therapy, 23*(3), 263-281. doi: 10.1080.08098131.2013.854269

Kim, J. (2015). Music Therapy with Children who have been Exposed to ongoing Child abuse and Poverty: A pilot Study. *Nordic Journal of Music Therapy, 24*(1), 27–43. doi: http://dx.doi.org/10.1080/08098131.2013.872696

Kjøli, J., & Ogden, T. (2013). Fellesfaktorer: ingen kur for alt. *Tidsskrift for Norsk Psykologforening, 50*(3), 263–265.

Knoblau, S. H. (2000). *The Musical Edge of Therapeutic Dialogue.* Hillsdale, NJ, and London: Analytic Press.

Kolnes, R. D. (1998). *Myten om det velintegrerte menneske.* Oslo: Genesis.

Kruse, B. (2016). *Thinking Art: Interdisciplinary Perspectives on Applied Aesthetics.* Oslo: NMH-publikasjoner 2016.

Krüger, V. (2012). *Musikk—Fortelling—Fellesskap. En kvalitativ undersøkelse av ungdommers perspektiver på deltagelse i samfunnsmusikkterapeutisk barnevernsarbeid* (Unpublished doctoral dissertation). University of Bergen, Bergen, Norway

Langer, S. (1942). *Philosophy in a New Key: A Study of Symbolism of Reason, Rite and Art.* New York: New American Library of World Literature.

Laugerud, T. (2012). Kirken i møte med åndelige erfaringer i grenselandet til kristen tro - et missiologisk perspektiv. *Tidsskrift for Praktisk Teologi, 29*(1), 4–12.

Lecourt, E. (1991). Off-Beat Music Therapy: A Psychoanalytic Approach to Autism. In K. E. Bruscia (Ed.), *Case Studies in Music Therapy* (pp. 73–98). Philadelphia: Barcelona Publishers.

Leder, D. (1990). *The Absent Body.* Chicago: University of Chicago Press.

Lee, C. (1996). *Music at the Edge: Music Therapy Experiences of a Musician with AIDS.* London and New York: Routledge.

Lévinas, E. (1961/2012). *Totality and Infinity: An Essay on Exteriority* (A. Lingis, Trans.). Pittsburgh: Duquesne University Press.

Lévinas, E. (1991). *Otherwise Than Being or Beyond Essence* (A. Lingis, Trans.). Pittsburgh: Duquesne University Press.

Levitin, D. J. (2007). *This is Your Brain on Music: The Science of a Human Obsession.* New York: Plume, Penguin Group.

Loewy, J. V., & Hara, A. F. (Eds.). (2007). *Caring for the Caregiver: The Use of Music and Music Therapy in Grief and Trauma* (2nd ed.). Silver Spring, MD: American Music Therapy Association.

Loos, G. K. (1994). *Spiel-Raüme der Magersucht. Musiktherapie und Körperwahrnehmung mit frühgestörten Pasienten* (Vol. 7). Stuttgard : Barenreiter Verlag, London: Gustav Fischer Verlag.

Lyons-Ruth, K. (1998). Implicit Relational Knowing: Its Role in Development and Psychoanalytic Treatment. *Infant Mental Health Journal, 19*(3), 282–289.

Malloch, S., & Trevarthen, C. (2009). *Communicative Musicality: Exploring the Basis of Human Companionship.* Oxford: Oxford University Press.

Malloch, S. (1999). Mothers and Infants and Communicative Musicality. *Musicae Scientiae,* special issue 1999-2000, pp. 29-53.

Maranto, C. D. (Ed.). (1993). *Music Therapy: International Perspectives.* Philadelphia: Jeffrey Books.

Marstal, I. (2008). *Barnet og musikken. Om betydningen af å stimulere barnets musikalske potensiale.* Copenhagen: Hans Reitzels Forlag.

Martin, R. (2007). *The Effect of a Series of Short GIM Sessions on Music Performance Anxiety* (Unpublished master thesis). University of Melbourne, Melbourne, Australia.

McFerran, K. S., Garrido, S., & Saarikallio, S. (2013). A Critical Interpretive Synthesis of the Literature Linking Music and Adolescent Mental Health. *Youth & Society, 20*(10), 1–18. doi: 10.1177/0044118X13501343

McKinney, C., Antoni, M. H., Kumar, M., Tims, F. C., & McCabe, P. M. (1997). Effects of Guided Imagery and Music (GIM) Therapy on Mood and Cortisol in Healthy Adults. *Health Psychology, 16*(4), 390–400.

Meadows, A. (2010). The evolution of GIM programming. *Voices. A World Forum of Music Therapy. 10*(3). Retrieved from https://voices.no/index.php/voices/article/view/497

Meltzoff, A. N., & Borton, R. W. (1979). Intermodal Matching by Human Noenates. *Nature, 282,* 403–404.

Meltzoff, A. N., & Gopnik, A. (1993). The Role of Imitation in Understanding Persons and Developing Theories of Mind. In S. Baron-Cohen, H. Tager-Fusberg, & D. Cohen (Eds.), *Understanding Other Minds: Perspectives From Autism* (pp. 335–366). Oxford: Oxford University Press.

Merleau-Ponty, M. (1962). *Phenomenology of Perception*. London: Routledge & Kegan Paul.

Metzner, S. (2016). Psychodynamic Music Therapy. In J. Edwards (Ed.), *The Oxford Handbook of Music Therapy* (pp. 448–471). Oxford: Oxford University Press.

Mulelid, M. J. (2004). *Den første kommunikasjonen.* (Unpublished master thesis), University of Oslo, Oslo, Norway

Mills, J. (Ed.). (2005). *Relational and Intersubjective Perspectives in Psychoanalysis: A Critique*. Hillsdale, NJ and London: Jason Aronson.

Mitchell, S. A., & Aron, L. (Eds.). (1999). *Relational Psychoanalyses: The Emergence of a Tradition*. Hillsdale, NJ and London: Analytic Press.

Moffitt, L., & Hall, A. (2003–2004). "New Grown with Pleasant Pain" (Keats): Recovering from Sexual Abuse with the Use of The Bonny Method of Guided Imagery and Music. *Journal of the Association for Music and Imagery, 9*, 59-77.

Montello, L. (2000, December). The Perils of Perfectionism. *International Musician*, 14–15.

Montello, L. (2003). Protect this Child: Psychodynamic Music Therapy with a Gifted Musician. In S. Hadley (Ed.), *Psychodynamic Music Therapy: Case Studies* (pp. 299–318). Gilsum, NH: Barcelona Publishers.

Mössler, K. (2010). "I am a Psychotherapeutically Oriented Music Therapist": Theory Construction and its Influence on Professional Identity Formation under the Example of the Viennese School of Music Therapy. *Nordic Journal of Music Therapy. 20*(2), 155-184, doi: 10.1080/08098131003768110

Mühlhausen, S. (n.d.). Er Henrik kommet? In S. Mühlhausen (Ed.), *14 Songs for improvisation* (p. 1). Køge: Forlaget SØM.

Myrstad, E. (2001). Vitenskap og reduksjonisme. *Tidsskrift for Norsk Psykologforening, 38*, 136–138.

Myskja, A., & Lindbæk, M. (2000). Hvordan virker musikk på menneskekroppen? *Tidsskrift for Norsk Lægeforening, 10*(120), 1182–1185.

Nerheim, H. (1995). *Vitenskap og kommunikasjon.* Oslo: Universitetsforlaget.

Nissen-Lie, H. (2012). Hva kjennetegner gode og mindre gode psykoterapeuter? Betydning av terapeutens selvforståelse for prosess og utfall av psykoterapi. *Mellanrummet, 26,* 70–81.

Nissen-Lie, H. A. (2013). Fellesfaktordebatt på ville veier. *Tidsskrift for Norsk Psykologforening, 50,* 489–491.

Nissen-Lie, H. A., Monsen, J. T., & Rønnestad, M. H. (2010, November). Therapist Predictors of Early Patientrated Working Alliance: A Multilevel Approach. *Psychotherapy Research, 20*(6), 627–646. doi: 10.1080/10503307.2010.497633

Nordoff, P., & Robbins, C. (1977). *Creative Music Therapy. Individual Treatment for the Handicapped Child.* New York: John Day.

Næss, T. (1981). *Den mystiske boks.* Oslo: Norsk Musikforlag A/S.

Næss, T., & Ruud, E. (2007). Audible Gestures: From Clinical Improvisation to Community Music Therapy. Music Therapy with an Institutionalized Woman Diagnosed with Paranoid Schizophrenia. *Nordic Journal of Music Therapy, 16*(2), 160-171, doi: 10.1080/08098130709478186

Odell-Miller, H. (2007). *The Practice of Music Therapy for Adults with Mental Health Problems: The Relationship between Diagnosis and Clinical Method* (Unpublished doctoral dissertation). Aalborg University, Aalborg, Denmark.

Odell-Miller, H., & Richards, E. (Eds.). (2008). *Supervision of Music Therapy: A Theoretical and Practical Handbook.* London: Routledge.

Oldfield, A., Tomlinson, J., & Loombe, D. (Eds.). (2015). *Flute, Accordion or Clarinet? Using the Characteristics of Our Instruments in Music Therapy.* London and Philadelphia: Jessica Kingsley Publishers.

Olsen, H. (2006). *Spiritualitet.* Kristiansand: Høgskolen i Agder.

Opsahl, C. P. (2012). *Dance to My Ministry: Exploring Hip-hop Spirituality* (Unpublished doctoral dissertation). University of Oslo, Oslo, Norway.

Papousêk, M., & Papousêk, H. (1981). Musical Elements in the Infant's Vocalization: Their Significance for Communication, Cognition and Creativity. In L. P. Lipsitt (Ed.), *Advances in Infancy Research. Vol. 1*, (163-224). Norwood, NJ: Ablex.

Pavlicevic, M. (1990). Dynamic Interplay in Clinical Improvisation. *British Journal of Music Therapy, 4*(2), 5-9.

Pedersen, I. N. (Ed.). (2013). *Kunstneriske medier i supervision af psykoterapi. Insigt og vitalitet.* Aalborg: Aalborg universitetsforlag.

Pedersen, I. N., & Mahns, W. (1996). *Nordic Network in Music Therapy Research 1993-1996.* NorFa Nordisk Forskerakademi: Aalborg University.

Peterlin, K., & Sloves, R. (1985). Time-limited Psychotherapy with Children: Central Theme and Time as Major tools. *Journal of The American Academy of Child Psychiatry, 24*(6), 788-792.

Pethybridge, E. (2013). Inner Spirit: Investigating how Music Therapists' Experiences of their Spirituality may be Relevant to their Work. *British Journal of Music Therapy, 27*, 40-51.

Piaget, J. (1954). *The Construction of Reality.* New York: Basic Books.

Pihl, M. (1989/2009). Dialog mellom indre og ytre muskellag kan føre til bedre fysisk og psykisk helse. In K. Ekerholt (Ed.), *Festskrift til Berit Heir Bunkan. HiO-rapport* (pp. 175-189). Oslo: Høgskolen i Oslo (vol. 10).

Pines, A., & Aronson, E. (1988). *Career burnout: Causes and cures.* New York: The Free Press.

Plessen, K. J., & Kabricheva, G. (2010). Hjernen og følelser: fra barn til voksen. *Tidsskrift for den Norske Legeforening, 130*(9), 932-935.

Polanyi, M. (1969). *Knowing and being.* Chicago: University of Chicago Press.

Polkinghorne, D. E. (1989). Phenomenological Research Methods. In R. S. Valle & H. Sten (Eds.), *Existential-Phenomenological Perspective in Psychology: Exploring the Breadths of Human Experience* (pp. 41-60). New York and London: Plenum Press.

Priestley, M. (1975/1985). *Music Therapy in Action* (2nd ed.). St. Louis, MO: MMB Music Inc.

Procter, S. (2002). Empowering and Enabling: Music Therapy in Non-medical Mental Health Provision. In C. Kenny & B. Stige (Eds.),

Contemporary Voices in Music Therapy (pp. 95-108). Oslo: UniPub Forlag.

Proskauer, S. (1971). Focused Time-Limited Psychotherapy with Children. *Journal of the American Academy of Child Psychiatry, 10*(4), 619-639.

Richards, R. (2007). Twelve Potential Benefits of Living more Creatively. In R. Richards (Ed.), *Everyday Creativity and New Views of Human Nature: Psychological, Social, and Spiritual Perspectives* (pp. 289-319). Washington, DC: American Psychological Association.

Richardson-Delgado, J. M. (2006). *Exploring Burnout and Renewal Among Music Therapy Faculty* (Unpublished doctoral dissertation). Minnesota: Capella University.

Ridder, H. M. O. (2003). *Singing in Individual Music Therapy with Persons Suffering from Dementia* (Unpublished doctoral dissertation). Aalborg University, Aalborg, Denmark.

Rogers, C. R. (1951/1965). *Client-Centered Therapy: Its Current Practice, Implications, and Theory.* Boston: Houghton-Mifflin.

Rogers, C. R. (1979). The Foundations of the Person-Centred Approach. Retrieved from http://www.elementsuk.com/libraryofarticles/foundations.pdf

Rogers, P. J. (1995). Sexual Abuse and Eating Disorders. A Possible Connection indicated through Music Therapy? In D. Doktor (Ed.), *Arts Therapies and Clients with Eating Disorders: Fragile Board* (pp. 262-278). London and Philadelphia: Jessica Kingsley Publishers.

Rolvsjord, R. (1996). Et interaksjonsperspektiv på musikkterapi: Hva vil et interaksjonsteoretisk perspektiv bety for å forstå musikken og samspillets funksjon i musikkterapi? *Musikkterapi, 1*, 15-31.

Rolvsjord, R. (2004). Therapy as Empowerment: Clinical and Political Implications of Empowerment Philosophy in Mental Health Practises of Music Therapy. *Nordic Journal of Music Therapy, 13*(2), 99-111.

Rolvsjord, R. (2010). *Resource Oriented Music Therapy in Mental Health Care.* Gilsum, NH: Barcelona Publishers.

Rolvsjord, R. (2014). The Competent Client and the Complexity of Disability. *Voices: A World Forum for Music Therapy, 14*(3). doi: 10.15845/voices.v14i3.787

Rolvsjord, R. (2015a). Five Episodes of Clients' Contributions to the Therapeutic Relationship: A Qualitative Study in Adult Mental Health Care. *Nordic Journal of Music Therapy.* Published online 23 Feb 2015. doi: 10.1080/08098131.2015.10 10562 .

Rolvsjord, R. (2015b). What Clients do to Make Music Therapy Work: A Qualitative Multiple Case Study in Adult Mental Health Care. *Nordic Journal of Music Therapy, 24*(4), 296-321. doi: 10.1080/08098131.2014.96475

Ruud, E. (1990). *Musikk som kommunikasjon og samhandling.* Oslo: Solum Forlag.

Ruud, E. (1997/2013). *Musikk og identitet* (2nd ed.). Oslo: Universitetsforlaget.

Ruud, E. (1998). *Music Therapy: Improvisation, Communication and Culture.* Gilsum, NH: Barcelona Publishers.

Ruud, E. (2005). Philosophy and Theory of Science. In B. L. Wheeler (Ed.), *Music Therapy Research* (pp. 33–44). Gilsum, NH: Barcelona Publishers.

Ruud, E. (1996). *Musikk og verdier.* Oslo: Universitetsforlaget.

Ruud, E. (2010). *Music Therapy. A Perspective from the Humanities.* Gilsum, NH: Barcelona Publishers.

Ruud, E. (2016). The Future of Theory in Music Therapy. In C. Dileo (Ed.), *Envisioning the Future of Music Therapy* (pp. 133-138). Philadelphia: Temple University.

Ryum, T., & Stiles, T. C. (2005). Betydningen av den terapeutiske allianse: En studie av alliansens prediktive validitet. *Tidsskrift for Norsk Psykologforening, 42*, 998–1003.

Rønnestad, H. M. (2000). Psykoterapiforskning: Noen utviklingslinjer og betraktninger om «the Dodo bird verdict»: «*Everybody* has won and *all* must have prizes». *Tidsskrift for Norsk Psykologforening, 37*, 1003–1016.

Rønnestad, H. M., & Orlinsky, D. E. (2006). Terapeutisk arbeid og profesjonell utvikling: En internasjonal studie. *Tidsskrift for Norsk Psykologforening, 43*(11), 1175–1178.

Saarikallio, S., Gold, C., & McFerran, K. (2015). Development and Validation of the Healthy-Unhealthy Music Scale. *Child and Adolescent Mental Health, 20*(4), 210-217. doi: 10.1111/camh.12109

Sachs, O. (2006). The Power of Music. *Brain, 129,* 2528-2532.

Sachs, O. (2007). *Musicophilia: Tales of Music and the Brain.* New York: Picador.

Safran, J. D., & Muran, J. C. (2000). *Negotiating the Therapeutic Alliance: A Relational Treatment Guide.* New York and London: Guildford Press.

Schanche, E., & Binder, P. E. (2006). Her og nå med Daniel Stern. *Tidsskrift for Norsk Psykologforening, 43*(9), 953–954.

Schei, E. (2009). Helsebegrepet: selvet og cellen. In E. Ruud (Ed.), *Musikk i psykisk helsearbeid for barn og unge,* (pp. 7-14). Oslo: NMH-publikasjoner 2009:5, Skriftserie fra Senter for musikk og helse, (vol. 2).

Schibby, A. L. L. (1991). The Role of "Recognition" in the Resolution of a Specific Interpersonal Dilemma. *Journal of Phenomenological Psychology, 24*(2), 175–189. doi: 10.1163/156916293X00134

Schibby, A. L. L. (1996). Anerkjennelse: En terapeutisk intervensjon? *Tidsskrift for Norsk Psykologforening, 33*(6), 530–537.

Schibby, A. L. L. (2009). *Relasjoner: Et dialektisk perspektiv på esistensiell og psykodynamisk psykoterapi.* Oslo: Universitetsforlaget.

Schwabe, C. (2005). Resource-Oriented Music Therapy: The Development of a Concept. *Nordic Journal of Music Therapy, 14*(1), 49–56.

Siegel, D. J. (1999). *The Developing Mind: Towards a Neurobiology of Interpersonal Experience.* New York: Guildford Press.

Skau, G. M. (1992). *Mellom makt og hjelp. En samfunnsvitenskapelig tilnærming til forholdet mellom klient og hjelper.* Oslo: TANO A.S.

Skårderud, F. (1998). *Turmoil: A Journey into the Contemporary Self.* Oslo: Aschehoug.

Skårderud, F., & Sommerfeld, B. (2008). Mentalisering: et nytt teoretisk og terapeutisk begrep. *Tidsskrift for Norske Legeforening, 128*(9), 1066–1069.

Sletvold, J. (2005). I begynnelsen var kroppen. Kroppen i psykoterapi: teoretisk grunnlag og terapeutiske implikasjoner. *Tidsskrift for Norsk Psykologforening, 42*(6), 497–504.

Small, C. (1998). *Musicking: The Meanings of Performing and Listening.* Hanover, NH: University Press of New England.

Smeijsters, H. (2012). Analogy and Metaphor in Music Therapy: Theory and Practice. *Nordic Journal of Music Therapy, 21*(3), 227–249.

Smith, J. A., Flowers, P., & Larkin, M. (2009). *Interpretative Phenomenological Analysis: Therapy, Method and Research.* London: Sage.

Sokolowski, R. (1974/1989). *Husserlian Meditations: How Words Present Things.* Evanston, IL: Northwestern University Press.

Solli, H. P., & Rolvsjord, R. (2015). "The Opposite of Treatment": A Qualitative Study of how Patients diagnosed with Psychosis experience Music Therapy. *Nordic Journal of Music Therapy, 24*(1), 67–92. doi: http://dx.doi.org/10.1080/08098131.2014.890639

Sparre, M. (2009a). *Balansenøkler. Om å balansere kroppen og livet.* Oslo: Tropos forlag.

Sparre, M. (2009b, Aug 28). *Fra eple til frukt: Musikere og helse i et nytt paradigme.* Paper presented at Seminar on Musician and Health, Fagdag: Musikere og helse Oslo, Norges musikkhøgskole.

Stensæth, K. (2008). *Musical Answerability: A Theory on the Relationship between Music Therapy Improvisation and the Phenomenon of Action* (Unpublished doctoral dissertation). Norwegian Academy of Music, Oslo, Norway.

Stensæth, K. (2014). Leg og musikterapi. In L. O. Bonde (Ed.), *Musikterapi: Teori, uddannelse, praksis, forskning* (pp. 138-146). Aarhus: KLIM.

Stensæth, K., & Trondalen, G. (2012). Dialogue on Intersubjectitvity: Interview with Stein Bråten and Colwyn Trevarthen. *Voices. A World Forum for Music Therapy, 12*(3). Retrieved from https://normt.uib.no/index.php/voices/article/view/682/568

Stern, D. N. (1971). A Micro-Analysis of Mother-Infant Interaction: Behavior Regulating Social Contact between a Mother and her

3 1/2-Month-Old Twins. *Journal of the American Academy of Child Psychiatry, 10*(3), 501–517.

Stern, D. N. (1984). Affect Attunement. *Frontiers of Infant Psychiatry, 2*, 3–14.

Stern, D. N. (1985). *The Interpersonal World of the Infant. A View from Psychoanlaysis and Developmental Psychology.* New York: Basic Books.

Stern, D. N. (1995). *The Motherhood Constellation.* New York: Basic Books.

Stern, D. N. (1996, November 15). *How do People Change in Psychotherapy Through Non-Verbal Means?* Paper presented at the Nordic Network for Music Therapy Research, Gml. Vraa Slot [Old Vraa Castle]. NorFa Nordisk Forskerakademi: Aalborg University

Stern, D. N. (1998). The Process of Therapeutic Change Involving Implicit Knowledge: Some Implications of Developmental Observations for Adult Psychotherapy. *Infant Mental Health Journal, 19*(3), 300–308.

Stern, D. N. (2000). *The Interpersonal World of the Infant: A View from Psychoanalysis and Developmental Psychology.* New York: Basic Books.

Stern, D. (2004). *The Present Moment In Psychotherapy and Everyday Life.* New York and London: W. W. Norton & Company.

Stern, D. N. (2010). *Forms of Vitality: Exploring Dynamic Experience in Psychology, the Arts, Psychotherapy, and Development.* Oxford and New York: Oxford University Press.

Stern, D. N., Hofer, L., Haft, W., & Dore, J. (1985). Affect Attunement: Sharing of Feeling States between Mother and Infant by Means of Inter-modal Fluency. In T. M. Field & N. D. Fox (Eds.), *Social Perception in Infants* (pp. 249–268). Nerwood, NJ: Belx Publishing.

Stern, D. N., Sander, L. W., Nahum, J. P., Harrison, A. M., Lyons-Ruth, K., Morgan, A. C., Brushweiler-Stern, N., Tronick, E. Z. (1998). Non-interpretive Mechanisms in Psychoanalytic Therapy: The "Something more" than Interpretation. *International Journal of Psychoanalysis, 79*, 903–921.

Stige, B. (2002). *Culture-centered Music Therapy*. Gilsum, NH: Barcelona Publishers.

Stige, B. (2003). *Elaborations toward a Notion of Community Music Therapy*. (Unpublished doctoral dissertation). University of Oslo, Oslo, Norway.

Stige, B., Malterud, K., & Midtgarden, T. (2009). Toward an Agenda for Evaluation of Qualitative Research. *Qualitative Health Research, 19*(10), 1504–1516. doi: 10.1177/1049732309348501

Sting. (1987). "Fragile." [Producer Sting, Padgham H., Loren B. and Neil Dorfsman]. On *Nothing like the Sun* [CD]. Montserrat: Air Studios, A &M 75021-6402-2

Stolorow, R., Atwood, G., & Brandtchaft, B. (Eds.). (1994/2004). *The Intersubjective Perspective*. Oxford: Rowman & Littlefield.

Storheim, E. (1993). Immanuel Kant. In T. B. Eriksen (Ed.), *Vestens tenkere. Fra Descartes til Nietzsche* (Vol. 2, pp. 242-264). Oslo: Aschehoug.

Strehlow, G. (2009). Mentalisierung und ihr Nutzen für die Musiktherapie. *Musiktherapeutische Umschau, 30*(2), 89–101. doi: 10.13109/muum.2009.30.2.89

Strehlow, G. (2013). Mentalisierung und ihr Bezug zur Musiktherapie. *Musiktherapeutische Umschau, 34*(2), 135–145. doi: 10.13109/muum.2013.34.2.135

Stålsett, G. (2012). *Existential and Religious Issues in Psychotherapy: Development and Evaluation of a new Integrative Treatment Model (VITA) for Comorbid Depressive Disorders* (Unpublished doctoral dissertation). University of Oslo, Oslo, Norway.

Sundberg, O. K. (1980). *Pythagoras og de tonende tall*. Oslo: Nordli A/S.

Sutton, J. P. (2003). "The Pause That Follows": Silence, Improvised Music and Music Therapy. *Nordic Journal of Music Therapy, 11*(1), 27–38.

Svendsen, B. (2016). Allianse. Hva, hvorfor og hvordan? In H. Haavind & H. Øvreeide (Eds.), *Barn og unge i psykoterapi. Samspill og utviklingsforståelse* (2. ed.) (pp. 49-64). Oslo: Gyldendal akademisk.

Theorell, T. (2009). *Noter om musik och hälsa*. Stockholm: Karolinska Institutet, University Press.

Thompson, G. M. (2005). Phenomenology of Intersubjectivity: A Historical Overview of the Concept and its Clinical Implications. In J. Mills (Ed.), *Relational and Intersubjective Perspectives in Psychoanalysis: A Critique* (chapter 2). Hillsdale, NJ and London: Jason Aronson.

Thorsteinsson, V. W. (2000). Perspektiver på selvbegrepet. In A. Johnsen, R. Sundet & V. W. Thorsteinsson (Eds.), *Samspill og selvopplevelse. Nye veier i relasjonsorienterte terapier* (pp. 36–53). Oslo: TANO Aschehoug.

Trevarthen, C. (1980). The Foundations of Intersubjectivity: Development of Interpersonal and Cooperative Understanding in Infants. In D. R. Olson (Ed.), *The Social Foundations of Language and Thought* (pp. 316–342). New York: Norton.

Trevarthen, C. (1999). Musicality and The Intrinsic Motive Puls: Evidence from Human Psychobiology and Infant Communication. *Musicæ Scientiæ. Escom European Society for the Cognitive Sciences of Music* (Special issue 1999–2000), 155–215.

Trevarthen, C., & Hubley, P. (1978). Secondary Intersubjectivity. In A. Loch (Ed.), *Action, Gesture, and Symbol* (pp. 183–229). London: Academic Press.

Trevarthen, C., & Malloch, S. (2000). The Dance of Wellbeing: Defining the Musical Therapeutic Effect. *Nordic Journal of Music Therapy*, *9*(2), 3–17.

Trolldalen, G. (1997a). *Musikkterapi og samspill. Et musikkterapiprosjekt for mor og barn.* (Unpublished master thesis). University of Oslo, Oslo, Norway.

Trolldalen, G. (1997b). Music Therapy and Interplay. A Music Therapy Project with Mothers and Children Elucidated through the Concept of "Appreciative Recognition." *Nordic Journal of Music Therapy*, *6*(1), 14–27.

Trondalen, G. (2001). Visible Through an Audible Voice: A Music Therapy Study with a Female who had ceased Talking. *British Journal of Music Therapy*, *15*(2), 61–68.

Trondalen, G. (2003). "Self-listening" in Music Therapy With a Young Woman Suffering from Anorexia Nervosa. *Nordic Journal of Music Therapy*, *12*(1), 3–17.

Trondalen, G. (2004a). *Klingende relasjoner. En musikkterapistudie av "signifikante øyeblikk" i musikalsk samspill med unge mennesker med anoreksi* (Unpublished doctoral dissertation). Norwegian Academy of Music, Oslo, Norway.

Trondalen, G. (2004b). *Jakten på det integrerte menneske: En studie av 30-GIM reiser med fokus på symboler og bilder.* (Unpublished final thesis, Guided Imagery and Music), Danish Institute of GIM, Copenhagen, Denmark.

Trondalen, G. (2005a). Improvisasjon i musikkterapipraksis: Tradisjon, kunst, teknikk. In E. Nesheim, I. M. Hanken & B. Bjøntegaard (Eds.), *Flerstemmige Innspill. En artikkelsamling* (pp. 123–143). Oslo: NMH-publikasjoner 2005:1, (vol. 1).

Trondalen, G. (2005b). "Significant Moments" in Music Therapy with young Persons suffering from Anorexia Nervosa. *Music Therapy Today, 6*(3), 396–429.

Trondalen, G. (2007a). A Moment is a Moment is a Moment. Om gylne øyeblikk i musikkterapeutisk teori og praksis. *Psyke og Logos. Musik og psykologi, 28*(1), 574–593.

Trondalen, G. (2008). Musikkterapi: Et relasjonelt perspektiv. In G. Trondalen & E. Ruud (Eds.), *Perspektiver på musikk og helse. 30 år med norsk musikkterapi,* (pp. 29-48). Oslo: NMH-publikasjoner 2008:4, Skriftserie fra Senter for musikk og helse, (vol. 1).

Trondalen, G. (2009-2010). Exploring The Rucksack of Sadness: Focused, Time-Limited Bonny Method of Guided Imagery and Music with a Female Executive. *Journal of the Association for Music and Imagery, 12*, 1–20.

Trondalen, G. (2010, November). The Flute and I: The Bonny Method of Guided Imagery and Music with a Young Man. *Voices. The World Forum for Music Therapy.*

Trondalen, G. (2011). Music is about feelings: Music Therapy with a young Man suffering from Anorexia Nervosa. In T. Meadows (Ed.), *Developments in Music Therapy Practice: Case Examples* (pp. 434–452). Gilsum, NH: Barcelona Publishers.

Trondalen, G. (2012, 21 Sept). *Music: A Stairway to Heaven? On Spirituality and Guided Imagery and Music.* Keynote address at the 10th European Conference on Guided Imagery and Music, Vadstena, Sweden.

Trondalen, G. (2013a). Author's Personal Narrative. In L. O. Bonde, E. Ruud & M. S. Skånland (Eds.), *Musical Life Stories. Narratives on Health Musicking* (pp. 348–349). Oslo: NMH-publikasjoner 2013:5, Skriftserie fra Senter for musikk og helse. (vol. 5).

Trondalen, G. (2013b). Musical Performance as Health promotion. A Musician's Narrative. In L. O. Bonde, E. Ruud & M. S. Skånland (Eds.), *Musical Life Stories. Narratives on Health Musicking* (pp. 181–199). Oslo: NMH-publikasjoner 2013:5, Skriftserie fra Senter for musikk og helse. (vol. 5).

Trondalen, G. (2013c). Musicians. In L. Eyre (Ed.), *Guidelines for Music Therapy Practice in Mental Health* (pp. 840–872). Gilsum, NH: Barcelona Publishers.

Trondalen, G. (2013d). Present Moments. Obituary: Daniel Norman Stern. *Nordic Journal of Music Therapy, 22*(1), 3-6.

Trondalen, G. (2015). Expressive and Receptive Music Therapy in Eating Disorder Treatment. In A. Heiderscheit (Ed.), *Creative Arts Therapies in Eating Disorders Treatment* (chapter 5). London and Philadelphia: Jessica Kingsley Publishers.

Trondalen, G. (2016a). Resource-oriented Bonny Method og Guided Imagery and Music (R-oGIM) as a Health Resource for Musicians. *Nordic Journal of Music Therapy*, 205-240. doi: http://dx.doi.org10.1080/08098131.2014.987804

Trondalen, G. (2016b). Self Care in Music Therapy: The Art of Balancing. In J. Edwards (Ed.), *Oxford Handbook of Music Therapy* (pp. 938–958). Oxford: Oxford University Press.

Trondalen, G. (2016c). The Future of Music Therapy and Eating Disorders. In C. Dileo (Ed.), *Envisioning the Future of Music Therapy* (pp. 31-44). Philadephia: Temple University.

Trondalen, G. (In press). Musikkterapi som anerkjennelse: En mor-barn gruppe innenfor rammen av barnevernet. In K. Stensæth, V. Krüger, & S. Fuglestad (Eds.), *I transitt, mellom til og fra: Om musikk og deltagelse i barnevern.* Oslo: NMH-publikasjoner 2016:5. Skriftserie fra Senter for musikk og helse, (vol. 9).

Trondalen, G., & Bonde, L. O. (2012). Music Therapy: Models and Interventions. In R. MacDonald, G. Kreutz, & L. Mitchell (Eds.),

Music, Health and Wellbeing (pp. 40-62). Oxford: Oxford University Press.

Trondalen, G., & Skårderud, F. (2007). Playing with Affects and the Importance of "Affect Attunement." *Nordic Journal of Music Therapy, 16*(2), 100–111.

Trondalen, G., & Wosch, T. (In press). Microanalysis in Reflexive Research. In B. Wheeler & K. Murphy (Eds.), *Research in Music Therapy* (3rd ed). Gilsum, NH: Barcelona Publishers.

Tronick, E. Z. (1989). Emotions and Emotional Communication in Infants. *American Psychologist, 44*(2), 112–119.

Tronick, E. Z. (1998). Dyadically Expanded States of Consciousness and the Process of Therapeutic Change. *Infant Mental Health Journal, 19*(3), 290–299.

Tulving, E. (1972). Episodic and Semantic Memory. In E. Tulving & W. Donaldson (Eds.), *Organization of Memory* (pp. 381-404). New York: Academic Press.

Tønsberg, G. H., & Hauge, T. S. (1996). The Temporal Structure of Prelingustic Interaction. *Nordic Journal of Music Therapy, 5*(2), 63–75.

Ulvenes, P. G., Berggraf, L., Hoffart, A., Stiles, T. C., Svartberg, M., McCullough, L., & Wampold, B. E. (2012). Different Processes for Different Therapies: Therapist Actions, Therapeutic Bond, and Outcome. *Psychotherapy, 49*(3), 291–302. doi: 10.1037/ a0027895

Van Manen, M. (1990). *Researching Lived Experience: Human Science for an Action Sensitive Pedagogy.* London, Ontario: State University of New York Press.

Vega, V. P. (2010). Personality, Burnout, and Longevity among Professional Music Therapists. *Journal of Music Therapy, 47*(2), 155–179.

von der Fehr, D. (2008). *Når kroppen tenker.* Oslo: Universitetsforlaget.

Waldman, J., & Clark, M. F. (2013). *Stand, Flow, Shine: Caring for the Woman Within.* Piney Creek Studio, USA.

Wheeler, B. (2012). Ninth World Congress of Music Therapy: Interview with Mary Adamek, Kenneth Aigen and Al Bumanis. *Voices. A World Forum for Music Therapy, 12*(1). Retrieved from https://voices.no/index.php/voices/article/view/615/508

Wigram, T., Saperston, B., & West, R. (Eds.). (1995). *The Art & Science of Music Therapy: A Handbook*. Chur: Harwood Academic Publishers.

Winnicott, D. W. (1971). *Playing and Reality*. London and New York: Tavistock/Routledge.

Wolff, P. H. (1996). The Irrelevance of Infant Observations for Psychoanalysis. *Journal of American Psychoanalytic Association, 42*(2), 369–392.

Wolgien, C. S., & Coady, N. F. (1997). Good Therapists' Beliefs About the Development of Their Helping Ability: The Wounded Healer Paradigm Revisited. *Clinical Supervisor, 15*(2), 19–35. doi: 10.1300/J001v15n02_02

Wormnes, B. (2013). *Behandling som virker: Relasjonens, alliansens og kontekstens betydning*. Oslo: Cappelen Damm Akademisk.

Wosch, T., & Wigram, T. (2007). *Microanalysis in Music Therapy: Methods, Techniques and Applications for Clinicians, Researchers, Educators and Students*. London: Jessica Kingsley Publishers.

Yalom, I. D. (2001). *The Gift of Therapy: Reflections on Being a Therapist*. London: Judy Piatkus Ltd.

Zimmermann, M. (2000). Empowerment Theory: Psychological, Organizational and Community Levels of Analyses. In J. Rappaport & E. Seidman (Eds.), *Handbook of Community Psychology* (pp. 43–63). New York: Academic/Plenum Publishers.

Zur, O. (2015). *Power in Psychotherapy and Counseling*. Zur Institute. Retrieved from http://www.zurinstitute.com/power_in_therapy.html

Index